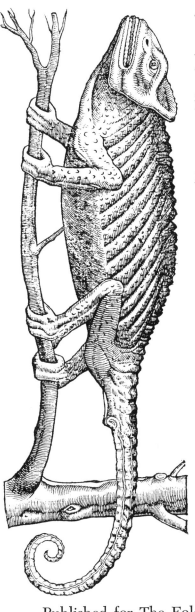

The Development of
Natural History
in Tudor England

F. D. and J. F. M. Hoeniger

Published for The Folger Shakespeare Library

The University Press of Virginia

The University Press of Virginia
Copyright © 1969 by the Folger Shakespeare Library

First published 1969
Second printing 1973

Cover illustration from plate 2
Title-page illustration from plate 10

Standard Book Number: 8139–0263–0
Library of Congress Catalog Card Number: 69–17336
Printed in the United States of America

Plates

Folger Booklets on Tudor and Stuart Civilization is a series designed to describe various aspects of the cultural history of the sixteenth and seventeenth centuries. A companion booklet to the present one is *The Growth of Natural History in Stuart England: From Gerard to the Royal Society,* also by F. D. and J. F. M. Hoeniger. Other titles in the series of related interest are: *Early English Gardens and Garden Books* by Ellen C. Eyler, *English Sports and Recreations* by Lilly C. Stone, *The Yeoman in Tudor and Stuart England* by Albert J. Schmidt, and *Dutch Influences on English Culture, 1558–1625* by D. W. Davies.

Introduction. By about 1680 not only the professional but also the lay Englishman had a very different outlook toward plants and animals from that of his forefathers of the early sixteenth century. Of the two Folger Booklets which trace the several stages of this development, this is the first, taking us to approximately 1600. It describes the activities and manner of thinking of some of the men who played an important role in this process of change and introduces the reader to a number of herbals and animal books of the period. The second booklet carries the study on to the founding of the Royal Society.

As the study of plants and animals in England did not proceed in isolation but was often influenced by developments on the Continent, while in turn some Englishmen made major contributions to writings by Continental biologists, our account will not always confine itself strictly to the English scene. However, only those Continental developments will be described without which the gradual changes in the study of nature in England cannot be seen in their true perspective. A number of important Continental writers on plants or animals will therefore hardly be mentioned in this survey. Further, this account will only barely refer to some pursuits which involve man closely with certain plants or animals but which contribute at most indirectly to his botanical or zoological knowledge. Every gentleman of the Renaissance knew about the habits of certain animals of the hunt and was well versed in the art of falconry: this subject is treated in the Folger Booklet on *English Sports and Recreations* by Lilly C. Stone. Agriculture is another large subject requiring a treatment of its own. Yet another Folger Booklet by Ellen C. Eyler is devoted to the gardens of great Tudor and Stuart houses. Dutch influences on English farming and gardening are discussed in D. W. Davies' booklet, *Dutch Influences on English Culture, 1558–1625*. Nor does the present survey cover the great advances of medicine during the period under review, though for a large part of it, as will be seen, the study of plants and also, to a lesser extent, of animals was mainly undertaken by medical men. As for men of religion and poets, we shall see that they often clung to lore of the past long after it had been abandoned by men who chose to examine data in the field.

The poets and their modern editors should perhaps bear part of the blame for the still widespread underestimation of the advances which were made in botany and zoology between the beginning of the sixteenth century and the advent of the Royal Society. From scholarly footnotes to works of Shakespeare's or even Milton's age, readers might infer that the most important English publications of the time on natural history were Philemon Holland's translation of Pliny (1601), Batman's shortened and revised edition of Bartholomaeus Anglicus (1582), Gerard's *Herbal* (1597), and Topsell's two animal books (1607, 1608). How inferior the latter two works are relative to others of their period will be shown later in this booklet and in its continuation, *The Growth of Natural History in Stuart England: From Gerard to the Royal Society*. Batman's *Bartholomew* was a conservative attempt to revive the gradually fading interest in the medieval encyclopedist Bartholomaeus Anglicus (about whom more below); and in the light of a fuller knowledge of botanical and zoological studies in the later sixteenth century, we are not surprised to find that the folio appeared in a single edition only. Philemon Holland's translation of Pliny (*The History of the World, Commonly Called the Natural History*, 1601) was almost as conservative as Batman. Holland himself knew nothing about natural history and evidently was unaware that more than a century earlier Pliny had been criticized for literally thousands of errors by two Italian students of flora, Ermalao Barbaro and Niccolò Leoniceno (both published in 1492), and that humanists of the sixteenth century were aware of the entirely derivative character of Pliny's biological survey. Moreover, Holland's folio, unlike several contemporary biological works, was unillustrated. It nevertheless was received with acclaim, partly because of Holland's personal and deserved prestige as a translator, partly because of the continuing fame which Pliny enjoyed among all but the most scientifically minded naturalists. When in 1646 Sir Thomas Browne wrote about the popular errors associated with animals in his *Pseudodoxia Epidemica,* he indicated that Pliny's *Natural History* "hath proved a powerful occasion of their propagation." The common man and poets were still under Pliny's spell long after his limitations had been proclaimed by humanists and scientists alike.

Many poets and other literary men continued to employ traditional animal and plant lore in their imagery long after its accuracy had come to be questioned, sometimes indeed after they themselves hardly believed in it anymore in a literal way, simply because they found it colorful, imaginative, and clear. Poets are often notoriously behind the times, from the scientist's point of view, and if not in outlook then in practice. In 1635 Francis Quarles prefaced his book of *Emblems* with the statement, "Before the knowledge of letters God was known by His hieroglyphics. And indeed what are the heavens, the earth, nay every creature, but hieroglyphics and emblems of His glory?"; thus he shows a much greater kinship with the standard assumptions of the Middle Ages than with the field biologists of his own day. The only qualification one would make is that his statement, if it had been made two or three centuries earlier, would have been received as unquestionably serious; by Quarles' time, it could not help sounding a bit quaint.

Another reason for the underestimation and even neglect of sixteenth- and early seventeenth-century biologists is the relatively small impact that they made on men's minds, by comparison with that of the astronomers, physicists, and certain medical innovators. We look in vain among the biologists for a Vesalius or Copernicus, a Kepler or Galileo. It may be for this reason that most popular surveys of the history of science or medicine convey the idea, or at least the implication, that biology remained medieval and did not develop at all significantly before John Ray

3

and Francis Willughby, Nehemiah Grew and Robert Hooke toward the end of the seventeenth century. But when the Royal Society was founded in 1660, we can be sure that the climate for it had been prepared by the quiet work of a number of impressive innovators and observers in the field over a period of more than a hundred years. However, at the same time it is well to realize that the activities of botanists and zoologists were less prone to disturb people's minds than those of Copernicus and the new cosmologers or than Harvey's discovery of the circulation of the blood in defiance of traditional, Galenic medicine. The discovery of new plants, the rejection of medieval approaches to plants and animals, the questioning of the most respected classical authorities on biology, the working out of a completely new system of plant or animal classification and thus of their interrelation: such activities make their impact relatively slowly and in subtle ways. Yet if this is true, it would be all the more unjust on the part of historians to ignore the courage and the searching of sixteenth-century botanists and zoologists. Fortunately, some historians of biology in our century have rectified this neglect by examining in detail the works and activities of several remarkable botanists and zoologists in this period. Our booklet is particularly indebted to the studies of Canon Charles E. Raven and Agnes Arber.

As we narrate the story of the gradual revolution in man's approach to nature in this period, we will try to take into account the large variety of factors and the professional men who contributed to its advance. Some credit, as will be shown, should go to artists and some to voyagers who explored new continents. Some should go to the early printers and to the woodcutters or engravers they employed. The humanists who sought to revive the classics by painstakingly editing the most reliable manuscripts they could find and the nationalists who fostered a pride in their native language had a share in the development of scientific observation. The Protestant Reformation was not only symptomatic of, but also further encouraged, attitudes of thought which questioned traditional assumptions and which bred individual – though sometimes wild and lawless – initiative.

4

The gradual growth of curiosity in plants and animals for their own sake must be seen in the context of the turbulent changes of power and thought in the period. This background will be borne in mind though our booklet must confine itself mainly to telling the story of those men who as scientists contributed to the emergent study of botany and zoology most directly.

The Medieval Attitude toward Natural History. Man has been interested in certain plants and animals ever since primitive times. On many of them he has depended for food, on others for clothing and decoration, on others again for medication. We can for instance assume that long before the period covered in this survey men inherited a wealth of practical knowledge about domestic animals and the vegetable crops on the farm. The country people of medieval England certainly appreciated the more abundant shrubs and wildflowers in bloom. The custom of bedecking one's sweetheart with wreaths of flowers on May Day dates back many centuries. Fairly widespread familiarity with some plants was moreover assured by traditional medicine, partly derived from folklore or folk knowledge and partly from Galen and other classical sources, which attributed to them all sorts of "virtues" with which to combat diseases. Gentlemen were trained to be expert in their knowledge of the animals of the hunt and particularly the various species of hawk employed in falconry, a widespread pastime in Europe at least since the time of Frederick II in the thirteenth century.

These kinds of knowledge involved, however, little of what one would call botanical or zoological study. There had been several works of considerable merit on plant and animal life in ancient Greece, especially those by Aristotle and Theophrastus. But the way medieval man was brought up seldom encouraged any analytical investigation. He took an interest in plants and animals not for themselves but because of their usefulness, real or assumed, in agriculture, sports, or medicine, and above all for the moral lessons which he was taught to derive from them.

This approach to nature, almost universally pervasive at the time, is so different from our own that it is very difficult for us to understand. Though men in the thirteenth century were no doubt as prone to be delighted by a charming landscape or to be frightened by a wild beast as we are, nature was held to be interesting not for itself but as a storehouse of symbols or intimations of a different and more perfect world. Such an outlook had been encouraged by the Church from its early days when it assimilated the method of allegorical interpretation from Alexandrian Neoplatonist scholars. Generalizing very broadly, the medieval Church taught that we can learn about God best through Christ, who is God's Incarnation and Word, but also through many other phenomena in the universe, physical and biological. From these, man can derive lessons of moral truth, some of which are quite overt, others of which lie so deeply hidden that they only reveal themselves to men endowed with unusual insight and grace. Why was nature thought to contain such lessons? Because the world we live in was believed to derive from and to depend upon another world in which alone man can find fulfillment or, as Platonists would say, perfection. Nature thus was interpreted by early and later Christian thinkers only for the sake of disclosing supernatural meaning, or insights into deeper reality.

Some of the lessons or explanations which were passed on from generation to generation in the Middle Ages were of the simple analogical kind. By watching lecherous sparrows man should be put on guard against similar vices in himself. Learning about the activities of night birds might help man beware of Satan. The charitable act of self-sacrifice of the pelican mother, which was believed to pierce its breast with its beak so that its own lifeblood could sustain its young, would remind man of the greater charity and the self-sacrificing blood of Christ and thus make him feel ashamed of his own selfish ways. Often, however, such purely analogical interpretations were rejected as inadequate because of the corruption of nature. For nature was thought to have fallen with man, and animals were held to be lower in the order of creation than man since they are not endowed with "reason" with which to control their passions or

6

appetites. Thus elaborate and ingenious allegorical interpretations were devised to discover in an animal's conduct the true lessons for man which God in His divine wisdom has hidden from all those not especially enlightened by grace.

Once this basic manner of studying nature, derived from a Christianized Neoplatonic outlook, is grasped, one will not be surprised to hear that medieval treatises on animals are remarkable for their lack of realism and their inclusion of much that is purely fanciful. Certain simple facts which could hardly escape anyone's observation were still presented accurately; as for instance that owls hunt by night or that house martins build their nests under eaves. But many natural phenomena had gradually, in the course of transmission, become incredibly distorted, sometimes as the result of semantic misunderstanding. For instance the leopard and the panther were for a long time regarded as the same animal because the two Latin names for leopard, *panthera* and *pardus*, reached England long before the animals did, and the ostrich was frequently confused with the Ostour (Astur) or goshawk. To them were added many bits of fantastic lore. Such lore established itself firmly because it often made more fascinating reading than the accounts of natural data and provided even more interesting material for allegorical interpretation. People did not check whether the creatures really existed or behaved in the manner described, for natural phenomena were held to be of little account in themselves. Often indeed previous literature provided the only possible source of knowledge about them. What mattered were the lessons that could be drawn from them. But the eagerness of some of the authors to entertain, and not only to instruct, no doubt had something to do with the gradual accumulation of fantastic lore.

Surveys of plants and animals in the Middle Ages were mainly of three kinds: herbals whose object was purely medical – later we will describe some early sixteenth-century versions; specific works on animals which were ultimately derived from the *Physiologus* (second century B.C.) and known as bestiaries; and the sections devoted to plants, animals, and minerals in the medieval encyclopedias. Of the latter two, the bestiaries were much

7

shorter and more obviously designed for entertainment, though they shared the moral earnestness of purpose and basic spiritual aim of the more comprehensive encyclopedias. The following extract from a Latin bestiary recently translated by T. H. White can be regarded as typical:

There is a bird called the YBIS (Ibis) which cleans out its bowels with its own beak. It enjoys eating corpses or snakes' eggs, and from such things it takes food home for its young, which comes most acceptable. It walks about near the seashore by day and night, looking for little dead fish or other bodies which have been thrown up by the waves. It is afraid to enter the water because it cannot swim.

This bird is typical of Carnal Man, who goes in for deadly dealings as if they were good spiritual food – by which his miserable soul gets nourished for punishment.

You, on the other hand, good Christian fellow – who are born again by water and the Holy Spirit to enter into the spiritual oceans of God's mysteries – on you he bestows the very finest food which he mentioned to the apostles, saying: "The fruit of the Spirit moreover is affection, praise, peace, forbearance, long suffering, etc." [T. H. White, *The Book of Beasts* (London: Jonathan Cape, 1954), pp. 119–20].

Descriptions like the above are preceded by schematic illustrations of the animal in question, which are often hard to recognize and sometimes entirely fanciful.

The aim of medieval encyclopedias was no less than to present a systematically organized account of the whole of creation. The two foremost examples by Englishmen, though both written in Latin, were *De naturis rerum* by Alexander Neckam and *De proprietatibus rerum* by Bartholomaeus Anglicus. The latter work proved particularly popular. John Trevisa's English translation of it was printed *ca.* 1497 by Wynkyn de Worde and again in 1535 by Berthelet. As late as 1582, Stephen Batman reissued it with omissions and additions as *Batman upon Bartholome.*

De proprietatibus rerum is a vast but neat statement of medieval cosmology in nineteen books. The opening books are devoted to God, the angels, and the heavens; that is, those parts of creation which exist in their original purity, unaffected by the events of the fall of man and nature. Then follow several books devoted to man: first his Rational Soul which comes from above and is eternal; then his body with its four elementary qualities of heat and cold, dryness and moisture; man's role or status in the universe; age; sex; the diseases he is subject to; and so on. The tenth book provides a general traditional account of the four elements of fire, air, water, and earth which govern the general order of the sublunary world or the globe which men, animals, and plants inhabit. All classification of animals and plants and even of geological phenomena is derived from this basic theory (its more medical applications will be summarized later when we turn to herbals). But the section on the purest element, fire, contains nothing on living creatures, for none were believed capable of residing in it. Instead the account includes a treatment of flame, coal, sparks, and ashes. The survey of the next element, air, however, leads up to a discussion of the creatures of the air in Book XII. It begins with the chameleon, which was believed to live entirely on air, and continues with the various orders of birds, from the highest – the eagle which flies close to the sun and rarely descends – to the lowest – birds which find all their food on the ground. Then follows an account of the element of water and its creatures, fishes. Books XIV to XVI deal successively with "earth" in general, the world and its countries (or geography), and minerals which are "engendered in the earth within." Book XVII describes those things which "grow upon the earth," that is, trees and herbs; and the eighteenth book finally is devoted to animals, creatures that "have life and feeling on the earth."

Difficult as it may be for the modern reader to conceive, practically none of the descriptions of animals or plants in this work are based on direct observation. Almost all the material is derived from literary sources, including versions of the *Physiologus* and bestiaries, the *Etymologia* or *Origines* by the seventh-century Archbishop Isidore of Seville (a work which enjoyed tremendous authority throughout the Middle Ages), and the works of other Church Fathers, Pliny, and his compiler Solinus. Factual accounts, often distorted in the process of transmission, are mingled with legends or fables indirectly derived from classical sources or folklore. Yet these fables add greatly to the entertaining quality of some of the chapters in this work. Animals being ordered by the element in which they live, bees, gnats, grasshoppers, and locusts are included among birds, and moreover several of the birds are purely legendary, such as the caladrius and the phoenix. But the most disappointing section is the one devoted to trees and herbs, Book XVII. As herbs lend themselves less readily to fables than animals, the account here becomes quite monotonous. The plants described are usually either edible or of medical value. Of flowers of the garden, only the lily, the rose, and the violet are included.

From the biological point of view, the *De proprietatibus rerum* is thus anything but an impressive work. Yet Bartholomaeus Anglicus' encyclopedia reflects the typical medieval attitude toward natural history. Only a few great men of the thirteenth century, foremost among them St. Albert, insisted on a closer reexamination and sometimes questioning of the data which, usually originating with classical authors, had become obscured or confused in the work of the Church Fathers. It is important to realize that for many men, including most of the major poets, Bartholomaeus Anglicus remained the standard authority on natural history until close to Shakespeare's age.

Three Early English Books on Plants and Animals. In the attitude to natural history, England remained medieval until well after 1500. Only slowly were medieval authorities and habits of thought challenged, first by the movement of the revival of ancient learning known as humanism and then by the gradual advent of a more modern scientific spirit, which was at first largely an outgrowth of humanism itself but later inevitably came into conflict with it. But we are getting ahead of ourselves. Evidence of the persistent prestige which medieval encyclopedias with their surveys of animals, minerals, and plants enjoyed in Europe around 1500 is provided by their many printings, in Latin and vernacular languages. Moreover, all the books devoted to surveys of plants and/or animals that appeared during the first seventy-five years after the invention of printing (1450–51), other than editions of classical authors or collections of fables, are either directly or indirectly derived from medieval manuscript sources.

This is true, for instance, of the many editions between 1480 and 1520, in Latin, German, and other modern languages, of the *Hortus sanitatis*, a large compendium of plants and animals that emphasizes their uses, mainly medical. Only some of the illustrations in one or two of these editions have any claim to originality.

This derivative character is exemplified by the three earliest printed books on animals or plants that appeared in English. Of these the first, *The Noble Life & Natures of Man, of Beasts, Serpents, Fowls & Fishes That Be Most Known* by Laurence Andrew, *ca.* 1521, has a major claim to interest simply because it happens to be the earliest printed work in English that includes many pictures of animals. The work was identified correctly only a few years ago when the single complete copy now known was discovered. Noel Hudson, *An Early Version of Hortus Sanitatis* (1954) reprints it in facsimile.

At first glance *The Noble Life* looks like an original work. It has an impressive woodcut on the title page in which Pliny, Dioscorides, and Albertus Magnus appear above a score of amazing forms of life sporting their respective elements: air, water, and earth. The work begins, on its first five leaves, with a naïve account of man. Then the author turns to his main subject, animals, introducing first the lamb with the feeble justification: "In the beginning we have the lamb because he is the most meekest beast living for it offends nobody." But from here on the work reveals itself to be nothing but a translation of the animal sections of a Dutch work, *Der Dieren Palleys*, which itself was derived from the *Hortus sanitatis*. In other words, the function of the title page and the opening account of man in *The Noble Life* was to endow the book with a false air of originality. Not only the descriptions of animals but also the woodcut illustrations accompanying them are derivative. Almost square, crudely sche-

Plate 1. Eagle, primitively stylized. From
Hortus sanitatis (1536).

Plate 2. Eagle. From Konrad Gesner, *Historiae animalium*, Book III (1585).

matic, and often quite unrealistic, the woodcuts are poor copies of those in the *Hortus sanitatis* of 1491 (see Plate 1).

The content of the work marks, if anything, a decline from the medieval bestiaries. The lamb, for instance, is never really described. Further, as in many medieval works, the same animal, real or imagined, is sometimes introduced twice, simply because it was traditionally known by two different names. For instance, on pages 67–68 the regulus is pictured and described as a small serpent which was supposed to be able to slay any creature, including man, by mere sight; on pages 87–88 the same mythical animal is shown and discussed under the name of basiliscus (or basilisk). Similarly, after describing the ibis, the author introduces what he mistakes for a different bird, the ibos, of which he writes: "Ibos is a great strong bird in orient and is great enemy unto the horse and hath both the voice and cry like the horse; but it is a fearful cry to hear; and they drive the horses away with their cry out of the pasture, for they eat such meat as the horses doth." One can imagine how this fanciful tradition may have had some ultimate basis in factual experience. What is certain is that Laurence Andrew never saw an ibis nor even tried to see one. According to Noel Hudson, the work includes sixty-seven known animals plus five unidentified, seventy-seven birds plus three unidentified, a considerable number of fishes, and a few insects; but also twenty-one fabulous or purely mythological animals and birds, among them the cinnamon bird of Arabia and the mennon birds of Egypt, which are commonly encountered in medieval lore.

In 1525 and 1526 there appeared, independently of each other, the first two printed herbals of the English language, known respectively as Banckes' *Herbal* (named after its printer) and *The Great Herbal*. Both were almost purely medical in aim, like their medieval predecessors. For the modern reader to grasp the fundamental nature of these works and some of the later herbals, he needs to be acquainted with the medical theory that informs them. This theory, inherited by men of the Middle Ages from classical times, was based on the view of the four elements (which we already encountered in Bartholomaeus Anglicus);

14

the four principles, natures or humors; and the four degrees. It was held that man's health depended on the balance of four chief fluids or cardinal "humors" in his body: blood, phlegm, choler, and melancholy. Each of these humors corresponds to one of the elements and is characterized by two main attributes, its relative dryness or moisture and its relative coldness or heat. For instance, choler is governed by the element of fire and is hot and dry. Now in each man one of the fluids or humors is slightly dominant, and that decides his prevailing temperament. But if suddenly a man comes too strongly under the corrupting influence of one of the elements or humors – through an imbalance in his body, bad food, or the influence of impure air – his body or mind develops an infirmity, that is, he becomes sick. However, God has for the benefit of man endowed many plants with medical virtues, or more specifically with peculiar "humors" of their own, which make them suitable antidotes for diseases in man caused by the opposite humor. It is thus important for a physician not merely to be able to diagnose correctly the disease in his patient in terms of an imbalanced humor, but to know which herb may serve as a suitable antidote and at least a partial cure. For this he needs to know not only the peculiar "humor" of certain herbs, but also the "degree," that is to say, the sharpness or intensity with which it exists in them. For instance, a sixteenth-century herbal will provide the information that "coloquintida is hot and dry in the third degree." From this the physician knows first of all that the plant's peculiar humor is choler (hot and dry) and that it is therefore an antidote to diseases in man caused by the opposite humor, namely phlegm, which is cold and moist. But he knows further that coloquintida has this humor to a high degree, and that it should therefore be applied cautiously in small amounts. As Turner writes in the Introduction to the third part of his *Herbal* (1568), herbs which are hot in the first degree merely "increase the natural heat which cometh after the digestion and other natural workings, if they are taken in," but those which are hot in the third degree, like coloquintida, "if they be taken in, they cut in pieces, they draw, they heat very much and make a man thirsty."

Aided by this brief survey of medical theory, the reader will perhaps appreciate the following extract from the Preface of *The Great Herbal:*

Considering the great goodness of Almighty God, creator of heaven and earth, and all things therein comprehended to whom be eternal laud and praise, etc. Considering the course and nature of the four elements and qualities whereto the nature of man is inclined, out of the which elements issueth diverse qualities, infirmities, and diseases in the corporate body of man, but God of his goodness, that is creator of all things, hath ordained for mankind (which he hath created to his own likeness) for the great and tender love, which he hath unto him, to whom all things earthly he hath ordained to be obeisant, for the sustentation [i.e., sustenance] and health of his loving creature mankind, which is only made equally of the four elements and qualities of the same, and when any of these four abound or hath more domination, the one than the other, then it constraineth the body of man to great infirmities or diseases, for the which the eternal God hath given of his abundant grace, virtues in all manner of herbs to cure and heal all manner of sicknesses or infirmities to him befalling through the influent course of the four elements beforesaid, and of the corruptions and the venomous airs contrary the health of man. Also of unwholesome meats or drinks, or wholesome meats or drinks taken untemperately which be called surfeits, that bringeth a man soon to great diseases or sickness . . . . Wherefore brotherly love compelleth me to write through the gifts of the holy ghost showing and informing how man may be holpen with green herbs of the garden and weeds of the fields as well as by costly receipts of the apothecaries prepared [1529 ed., sig. ❧2r].

This passage should make some practitioners of modern medicine pause.

Yet on the whole *The Great Herbal* is scarcely more impressive than Laurence Andrew's animal book. It is in the main a translation of the French *Le grand herbier,* and its illustrations, schematic and roughly chiseled woodcuts similar to those in Andrew's work, are degraded copies from the *Herbarius zu Teutsch,* a German adaptation of the *Hortus sanitatis* (see Plates 3 and 5). The work contains almost no botanical information whatsoever but was designed purely for physicians as a handy compendium of herbs and their traditional remedies. Its only interest for the modern student is furnished by the listing of early English names of many plants. The arrangement of the herbs is, as in similar medieval works, roughly alphabetical. No attempt at classification is found. Indeed, because the aim was not to provide a survey of plants but a medical survey, the author was not reluctant from time to time to introduce the odd animal, stone, or mineral – with its particular medical uses. There is even a section on glass with a picture of a glassmaker. In the chapter on the fox, the picture shows a cock sitting on a tree behind the fox, recalling the well-known fable. The accompanying text, however, does not allude to it but merely repeats typical material from a bestiary: "Vulpis is a subtle beast, for when he is hunted then he keepeth his tail between his legs that he should not let him in his cunning, and when he seeth that the dogs be near him, then he pisseth in his tail and striketh [shaketh, 1539 ed.] in the eyes of the dogs, which stench and smart they may not suffer, and then they let him alone, and run no more after." This abstruse piece of traditional fancy is followed by recipes derived from the fox for the cramp, the stone, and the gout. Not all the recipes in the work are strictly for illness. Some are designed to guard one against forgetfulness, others help one to be merry. Notably abundant are prescriptions against melancholy, for the work catered to a time when Boccaccio's *De casibus* and Lydgate's *Fall of Princes* were widely read and the Dance of Death was a favorite entertainment.

The Great Herbal was printed four times: first in 1526, then in a straight reprint in 1529, and in an adjusted edition in 1539 without the illustrations but with a new index of the English names of herbs, and again in 1561.

Banckes' *Herbal* of 1525 appeared in at least a dozen reprints or editions by 1560, thus evidently proving the more popular of the two works in spite of its lack of illustrations. From our point of view, this popularity was deserved for it is much more charmingly written and its author, unlike that of *The Great Herbal*, at least attempted brief descriptions of the plants, though the book's purpose was as purely medical as that of the companion

Plate 3. Water lily, primitively stylized.
From *The Great Herbal* (1529).

Of the herbe called Nymphea.
Nymphæa candida.   Nymphæa lutea.

Plate 4. White and yellow water lily. From William Turner, *Herbal* (1568).

work. In the 207 chapters the herbs are arranged in roughly alphabetical order. In each case, the chapter heading gives the learned (Latin) name of the herb, while the text begins with its popular, native name or names. This is usually followed by a two- or three-line description of the plant, and only then by an account of the herb's medical virtues and the methods of preparing it for medicinal use. But in several instances, notably in his chapter on rosemary, the author enlivens his treatment by charmingly narrating legends or old superstitions associated with the plant. The reader is directed to "take the flowers and make powder thereof and bind it to the right arm in a linen cloth, and it shall make thee light and merry. . . . Also boil the leaves in white wine and wash thy face therewith . . . thou shalt have a fair face." As often in herbals, an index of the diseases for which remedies are described is provided, a handy reference guide for physicians. The source of the work is still a matter of some doubt, but it looks like a compilation of materials from different manuscript herbals, now lost, for the style is uneven and some herbs discussed in the first part appear again later. In spite of the brief descriptions of the plants, we can thus not be sure that the work's anonymous compiler indulged in any botanical investigations of his own.

Turner and the German Fathers of Botany. The three works just discussed are testimony to how firmly the medieval approach to plants and animals was still entrenched in early sixteenth-century England. In fact these works contain hardly anything which was not derived from late medieval works of a similar kind. Their authors repeated data about plants or animals from earlier books or manuscripts which were themselves part of a long tradition: there is no indication whatever that they engaged in any personal examination of plants or animals. And indeed this attitude toward botany and zoology was to persist widely for many more decades. Traditional lore was repeated by many authors until well into the seventeenth century.

Yet years before the appearance of Banckes' *Herbal* and *The*

Great Herbal, a teenager by the name of William Turner was actively engaged in botanizing, bird watching and studies of other animals in his native Northumberland. He was to become the author of a number of works on plants, which mark the beginning of botany as a serious study in England, and of the first book by an Englishman which is entirely devoted to birds. Turner is the father of English botany and of English ornithology. His further plan to publish the first systematic survey of the fishes of the British Isles was prevented by his sudden death in 1568.

Turner was born at Morpeth, Northumberland, *ca.* 1508–10. About his early years until he entered Pembroke Hall, Cambridge, in 1526, we would know nothing were it not for a number of references in his own later works and in the works of Konrad Gesner and other Continental authors to specific observations Turner made at or near Morpeth. C. E. Raven's *English Naturalists* (pp. 49–51) provides a full list of these allusions to Morpeth and to Turner's boyhood. Many of them are botanical, but perhaps the most startling is the following description and comment on a robin's nest, found in Turner's book on birds:

The Rubecula (i.e., robin) . . . nests . . . in the thickest briers and shrubs after this fashion. Where it finds oak leaves in plenty, or leaves like the oak, it builds its nest among the leaves themselves close to the roots of briers or the thicker shrubs: and when completed covers it with leaves as if with topiary work. Nor does access lie open to the nest on every side, but by one way alone is entrance gained. And at that place where it enters the nest the bird builds a long porch of leaves before the doorway and, on going forth to feed, closes the end with leaves. But, what I now describe, I first observed when quite a boy, nevertheless I am not going to deny that it may build otherwise. If any have observed another way of nesting, let them tell it, and they certainly will not a little gratify the students of such things, myself among the first. I have imparted truthfully to others what I saw [*Turner on Birds*, ed. A. H. Evans (Cambridge: Cambridge University Press, 1903), p. 157].

At Cambridge, Turner studied medicine and theology and came under the influence of Hugh Latimer and Nicholas Ridley.

These men encouraged in him a deep reverence for the ancients, especially Aristotle. He acquired a fair knowledge of Greek and studied the humanistic translations of Greek biological writings into Latin, notably Theodore de Gaza's translations of Aristotle's *Historia animalium, De partibus,* and *De generatione* and Theophrastus' *Historia plantarum.* These works are not merely far more scientific in spirit than most medieval writings, but also superior to the mere compilations from earlier authorities by such Roman writers as Pliny, Solinus, and Aelian, on which medieval biologists depended. Later on, more will be said about the impact of the revival of classical biology.

But Turner's main studies at Cambridge were in the Greek New Testament, with special emphasis on the interpretation of the Pauline Epistles. Fired by Latimer, he became an early and prominent member of the pioneering movement of the English Reformation. He was ordained deacon in 1536. In his preachings and early writings, he stressed the need for a return to the Scriptures and contrasted the old or scriptural teaching with the new and "impure" doctrines of the Catholic Church. No wonder that as a Gospeler, a Protestant of the extreme puritan wing, he soon got into difficulties with the authorities. In 1542, he departed with his wife for the Continent, whether voluntarily or by force is not known.

After some travel, he settled down to a further study of medicine in Italy at Ferrara and Bologna and there came into contact not merely with leading humanists, but also with some of the foremost European scholars of natural history. Thence he moved briefly to Switzerland where he certainly visited Konrad Gesner at Zürich, and probably also Leonhard Fuchs, who had published his great herbal in 1542, at Basel. Next he spent some time with Longolius at Cologne and saw his pioneering Latin study on birds through the press in 1544, after the latter's death. The climate having become more suitable for liberal Protestants, he then returned to England and was appointed Dean of Wells. During the next years we see him devoting considerable energies to Protestant pamphlet literature. When Mary Tudor ascended the throne in 1553 Turner, like many of his fellows, once more fled to the Continent where he spent several years. He returned to his deanery in 1558, under Elizabeth, and died at Wells in 1568, soon after the publication of the third and final part of his great herbal.

It seems amazing that a man of such a turbulent theological career should also have been a learned doctor and by far the most outstanding authority on botany in the England of his time. We have noted how his interest in botany developed during childhood. His first botanical book, the Latin *Libellus de re herbaria novus*, appeared in 1538. It seems at first sight a very slight work. A booklet of merely twenty pages, unillustrated, it simply lists plants alphabetically by what Turner regarded as their standard Latin names and then, in two to six lines each, comments on alternative Latin, Greek, and native English names. But a later comment by Turner himself in the Preface to his herbal of 1568 makes us aware of the aim and importance of the earlier work. There he relates how he wrote the Latin herbal while still a fellow of Pembroke Hall because English physicians were utterly ignorant of herbs, always trusting herbwomen or apothecaries of deficient learning. He points out that "as yet there was no English herbal but one [he evidently means *The Great Herbal*], all full of unlearned cacographies and falsely naming of herbs, and as then had neither Fuchsius, neither Matthiolus, neither Tragus written of herbs in Latin" – we will say more about these Continental botanists later. How could English physicians be expected to apply sound herbal remedies without first properly knowing the names of the herbs in both Latin and English! Turner thus set himself a task that had really never been faced before: to identify the plants mentioned in the classical treatises and to provide them with their corresponding English names. He selected his catalogue of plants not from medieval manuscript herbals or their derivatives, as his predecessors had done, but directly from the great Greek authorities Aristotle, Theophrastus, and Dioscorides. As he proceeded with his project, he became aware of some extremely difficult problems. Many of the plants described by classical authors were southern and thus unknown to Englishmen; frequently the same

English name had become popularly attached to a variety of different plants; and for many plants there were no local names at all. Later he was to face similar problems in his book on birds. No wonder that he did not always solve these difficulties perfectly. For instance, sometimes he misidentified a classical plant by comparing it or mistaking it for a "similar" English plant. But the *Libellus* constitutes the first systematic attempt at defining plants by proper names. To assess its pioneering achievement, one need only compare with the *Libellus* the index of English names of herbs which was contributed to the 1539 edition of *The Great Herbal:* there three-quarters of the so-called English names are nothing else but corrupt Latin. Turner's *Libellus* is the work of a humanist scholar who was also an enlightened nationalist and a responsible medical man. He wanted to supply English doctors with the information that would enable them to identify herbs correctly and thus treat their patients properly. Such a work could only be done by one knowledgeable in the masters of classical botany and also acquainted with the plants locally available.

Turner's next biological work was his treatise on birds, 1544, discussion of which will be deferred until later. His second botanical work, *The Names of Herbs*, 1548, was a greatly enlarged version in English of the *Libellus*, from a list of 134 basic names to one of nearly 400, not counting the varieties or "subspecies" mentioned. The arrangement is still alphabetical by Latin standard names – in modern scientific works, plants are still identified by their Latin names, for native names tend to vary from district to district. But the descriptions are now in English, and these are frequently followed by some mention of a specific place or the general habitat where the herb can be found. The following extract from the work is chosen almost at random:

Lepidium

Lepidium is well known in England and is called with a false name Dittany; Dutchmen call it Pfefferkraut. It groweth in Morpeth in Northumberland by a water called Wanspeke in great plenty alone, without any setting or sowing. It is hot in the fourth degree.

Libanotis

Libanotis, called in Latin Rosmarinus, is of three kinds, where we have none saving only Rosmarinum Coronarium, which we call in English rosemary, which groweth plenteously in gardens in England. It is hot in the second and dry in the first.

[Lichen]

Lichen is also called in English Liverwort, in Dutch Steinliberkraut, in French Hepatique; the apothecaries call it Hepaticam. It groweth upon stones and moist grounds, and where as the sun cometh not [1548 ed., sig. Elr].

The variety of English and German localities mentioned in the book conveys some idea of the impressive geographical range of Turner's botanizing, an activity the authors of Banckes' *Herbal* and *The Great Herbal* never dreamed of. Throughout his life, Turner was to seek out the localities of the less common plants in England and in several countries on the Continent.

Three years later, in 1551, William Turner's *A New Herbal* appeared. This however was only the first part of Turner's largest and most ambitious botanical study. The second part was published in 1562, the completed *Herbal* in three parts as a sumptuous folio dedicated to Queen Elizabeth in 1568, shortly before Turner's death. Turner's heavy ecclesiastical duties as Dean of Wells and frequent interruptions account for the long intervals between these dates. From 1553 to 1558 he was on the Continent as a Marian exile, and while at Wells he was often distracted from botanical studies by theological controversy. In the first two parts of the work, he describes all plants known to Greek and Roman authors; the third "entreats of these herbs whereof no mention is made neither of the old Grecians nor Latins."

The Preface or dedication to Queen Elizabeth makes interesting reading. After complimenting the Queen on her beautiful Latin and knowledge of other languages, he defends himself against any contemporary insinuation that his herbal contains little that is original but only what can be found in the works of Fuchs, Mattioli, and others. Turner admits that he learned much from the Italians and Germans but claims with justification that they learned as much from him. He states that whenever he could he examined plants for himself, not simply taking the word of others: "I went into Italy and into diverse parts of Germany, to know and see the herbs myself, and to know by practice their powers and working, not trusting only to the old herbwives and apothecaries (as many physicians have done of late years), but in the matter of simples mine own eyes and knowledge: Wherefore I have something of mine own to present and give unto Your Highness." To Italy and Germany, Turner might well have added several parts of his native country. Again he stresses that he regards it his national duty to enable English physicians to know the names of herbs and their characteristics, "for how can he be a good artificer that neither knoweth the names of his tools, neither the tools themselves when he seeth [them]?" Finally, he promises a book of the names and natures of fishes within Her Majesty's dominions, if he lives long enough. Alas, he did not.

As the Preface clearly intimates, the primary purpose of Turner's *Herbal* was that of providing physicians with a guide to herbs. Its aim was therefore similar to that of Banckes' *Herbal* or *The Great Herbal*. Botany is still treated as the handmaiden of medicine, and we can be sure that at least three out of four sixteenth-century men who bought a copy of Turner's herbal were doctors. (Several contemporary drawings of physicians in the process of consulting a herbal have survived.) However, Turner fulfilled his purpose with a degree of competence and with a thoroughness unmatched before. Though his herbal includes a few wrong identifications, Turner leaves his predecessors far behind in accuracy and range. The *Herbal* is the product of a lifelong wrestling with the problems of attaching the right Latin and English names to plants. With good reason, therefore, the work is frequently cited in the *Oxford English Dictionary*. As for dubious plant lore, one will look almost in vain for it among his pages. On the contrary, Turner exposes the impostors of mandrake roots who with their faked wares were capitalizing on the widespread belief that they resemble mankind in their male and female shapes (see Plates 5 and 6): "The roots which are counterfeited and made like little puppets . . . and such form as a man hath are nothing else but foolish feigned trifles and not natural. For they are so trimmed of crafty thieves to mock the poor people withal, and to rob them both of their wit and their money." From the popular tradition that he inherited, Turner rejected what was ignorant or confused. Instead, he returned to the great classical authorities, particularly Theophrastus and Dioscorides, for whom he had an immense respect.

Yet even these he often did not accept blindly but insisted on renewed observation or experiment, and, if the experiment failed to corroborate tradition, he was honest enough to say so. For instance, in his treatment of lucerne or alfalfa (he calls it medica or "medic fother"), he first provides the descriptions by Pliny and Dioscorides, then adds further detail which he has observed himself: "Beside these marks . . . I have marked, that it has a yellow flower," etc. Then he cites the virtues as listed by classical authors, but continues:

Thus far have I written to you the minds and experience of old authors . . . . Now it that I have proved myself, I will not refuse to show unto you, my countrymen. I have sown three kinds of medic fother, the least kind, the great smooth kind, and the great rough kind. . . . The great smooth kind, as I have proved, groweth into a marvelous great bush. . . . This have I proved diverse times, wherefore I dare be bold to write it [Part II, 1568, p. 53].

The practical effect of this description was far greater than he could have dreamed. He provided the recipe for growing alfalfa as a fodder crop.

It is these personal descriptions that not merely enhance the value and liveliness of his herbal but persuade one that Turner was as much a botanical observer in the strict modern sense as a reformer of medicine. Turner described in his herbal some 238 native species of which his account constitutes the first scientific English record. We know that he corresponded with Gesner and others, exchanging with them specimens and botanical descriptions. He aimed at an English list of local flora, surely a botanical rather than a medical venture. His constant questioning of accounts based on popular hearsay or even descriptions sanctioned

ℭ Mandrake the male.

ℭ Mandrake the female.

Plate 5. Mandrake root, male and female, as traditionally conceived. From *The Great Herbal* (1529).

Mandragoras masc.

Of the Mandrage.

Here are two kindes of Mandrag / the black which is the female/ which is called the letti= cer/with lesse leues and narrower then lettice/ whiche haue a strong sauor/ and are spred vpon þ grounde. And this kinde bereth ap= ples lyke vnto sorbapples / pale in coloure and well smellyng/wherein is conteyned sede/ lyke vnto the kir= nelles of peres. It hath rootes of a good bignes ij. or iij. one foldyng it self within an other. They are black with out/and whyte within/& they are couered with a thick barke. And thys kynde hath no stalke. The other kynde is the white Mandrag/ and it is called þ male. The leues of this are byg/white/brode and smouth as the bete lefe is. The apples of thys a= re twyse as byg as the apples of the other be/to a color turnyng toward saffron. They smell plesantly/ ioyned to a certayn greuousnes. This kinde of Mandrage I haue oft tymes sene in England/ & it is þ herbe that we call

Plate 6. Mandrake root and comment on the faking of its male and female shapes. From William Turner, *Herbal* (1568).

by classical authority made him a humanist of a very modernistic bent. His *Herbal* was therefore by far the most important and original botanical work that had as yet appeared in English; this in spite of the fact that it hardly intimates any conception of classification or the interrelationship of species. Nor does Turner mention some of the basic botanical phenomena then occupying his Continental contemporaries.

However, a most striking feature of the *Herbal* still remains to be commented on: the astonishingly beautiful and realistic woodcut illustrations whose quality is infinitely superior to those in *The Great Herbal*. We are only referring to them now because they are derived from a major development on the Continent, especially in Germany, in the art of botanical illustration which now requires our attention. Turner's illustrations were not original. He was fortunate in acquiring some four hundred wood blocks from the great herbal of the German botanist Leonhard Fuchs (see Plates 4 and 6).

The illustrations in fifteenth- and early sixteenth-century herbals had been, with the exception of only a few in the German *Gart der Gesundheit* of 1485, traditional and crudely stylized. Then a remarkable change occurred in Otto Brunfels' *Herbarum vivae eicones*, whose three parts were printed in 1530, 1531, and 1536. In it, the pictures are much larger, often full-folio in size, and render the various parts of plants, especially their leaves, with amazing exactitude of detail. Botanical illustration had been transformed from traditional stylization to modern realism.

How can one account for this revolutionary development? The primary inspiration came from the work of the great German artistic genius, Albrecht Dürer, and his followers. Almost completely on his own in northern Europe, and beginning in the last decade of the fifteenth century, Dürer produced a number of astonishingly realistic drawings and water-color studies of plants, some even arranged in their ecological setting, and of a few animals. These pictures were widely admired almost at once and imitated – they still are favorites on Christmas cards, and they look like the work of a skillful nature photographer (see

Plate 7. Columbine. Drawing by Albrecht Dürer (1526)
in the Albertina, Vienna. (Reproduced from *Albrecht
Dürer, Schriftlicher Nachlass* [1963], courtesy of
Progress-Verlag Johann Fladung GMBH.)

Plate 8. Star-of-Bethlehem and other plants. Drawing by Leonardo da Vinci in the Royal Library, Windsor. (Reduced in size. Reproduced from Leonardo da Vinci, *Croquis et dessins de botanique* [Vol. XIV of *Feuillets inédits de Léonard de Vinci;* Paris, 1901]).

Plate 7). Dürer trained his students in the precise observation of plants in the field. The habit was continued by many lesser-known German painters throughout the sixteenth century.

At about the same time in Italy, an artist of equal if not greater genius, Leonardo da Vinci, became similarly fascinated by the phenomena of nature, including biology. From the strictly scientific point of view, in botany as in physics, Leonardo was indeed still more forward-looking than Dürer, witness the morphological interest displayed in some of his studies of herbaceous plants, shrubs, and trees. He attempted to convey the structure or architecture of the entire plant and its flower which is evident not merely in his drawings (see Plate 8) but also in his comment on morphological and physiological phenomena in the sixth part of his *Tractate*. Likewise, he showed a keen interest in the photo-physiology of leaves and their nutrition and in the branching of trees. All his studies were aimed at discovering more about the secrets of plant life. But for some reason the immediate impact of Leonardo's botanical drawings was slighter than Dürer's – unless, as is quite possible, he inspired Dürer himself – perhaps because Leonardo was too far ahead of his own time, and because his students consolidated other discoveries than his morphological ones.

At any rate, it was the plant drawings of Dürer and his students that made people in Germany aware of the intolerable inadequacy of the primitively unrealistic illustrations of contemporary herbals. Pressure grew to renew the pictorial content of herbals, with Brunfels' *Herbarum vivae eicones* as the first major result.

However, it was probably not due to Brunfels himself but to his printer and publisher that one of Dürer's greatest pupils, the Strasbourg painter Hans Weiditz (possibly identical with the Petrarca master of Augsburg), was hired to make the drawings for the woodcuts. Indeed Weiditz was given the controlling share in the work so that Brunfels, a humanist of primarily philological interest, had to abandon some of his original intentions and play second fiddle by providing the accompanying descriptions to Weiditz' drawings. As there is little of particular distinction to Brunfels' text, this was probably not unfortunate, except in one way. If Brunfels had been allowed proper control, he might well have taken objection to the not insignificant number of Weiditz' drawings that present plants in withered, crushed, or otherwise damaged condition because he used poor specimens to draw from.

This defect was remedied by the second of the German fathers of botany, Leonhard Fuchs, in his famous herbal of 1542. This time, the author saw to it that only mature and undamaged specimens were illustrated. Sometimes, indeed, a flower or a leaf is placed in an unrealistic position for the sake of superior botanical demonstration, at the risk of misrepresenting strict fact. However, most of the illustrations are both artistically complete and botanically exact, to an extent perhaps never superseded. It was Fuchs's aim to provide not only in the text but even in the illustration a complete life history of a plant. So he showed the flower in all stages from bud to fruit, the leaves in their various stages of development, and usually the entire plant with its root; yet he allowed sufficient room to the artist. The original draftsman was Albrecht Meyer, and the woodcut engraver, Rudolf Speckle. The work was most carefully produced at Basel by Isengrin in 1542. Soon an octavo edition, with the cuts reduced in size, appeared, followed by many others, some piratical. The influence of the pictures was immense. Turner's woodcuts are derived from Fuchs, as we have seen. Indeed, Fuchs's pictures are still found in several nineteenth-century botanical works, and the best plant artists of our time are still deriving inspiration from Fuchs's herbal.

In carrying the story of German and Swiss botany on from Fuchs, no account need be given of Lonacher's herbal for it is entirely conventional and derivative. The third father of German botany, Hieronymus Bock, known as Tragus, was of all the Germans of the age perhaps the most ardent student of native plants in the wild. Like Turner, he provided many localities of plants. But unfortunately he knew little about art. The first edition of his herbal, in 1539, was unillustrated. The illustrations of the second edition, 1546, by David Kandel, closely imitate those in Brunfels and Fuchs. The specimens for them were provided, live or dried, by Bock himself. While many of the pictures are skillful and pretty, they show little of the originality of Weiditz or of the artists employed by Fuchs.

Many of Kandel's pictures appear once more in a history of plants by Valerius Cordus, 1561, but that work is of greater interest because it also includes fifty pictures by Konrad Gesner of Zürich. If Gesner had not died of the plague in 1565, he would have contributed more to the development of botanical illustration in the sixteenth century after Fuchs than anyone else. By the time of his death Gesner had assembled no less than 1,500 pictures, some as drawings, some as aquarelles, some already turned into woodcuts; only a few were published during his century. But among these few are the very first pictures ever in which parts of a plant are revealed under the magnifying glass – they appeared in an appendix to Josias Simmler's life of Gesner, *Vita Conradi Gesneri*, of 1566. This was a development that looks forward to the Royal Society and well beyond. Those of us familiar with the experience of having the inside of a flower presented in all its beauty under magnification when projected as a colored slide will appreciate what the invention of the small magnifying glass contributed to botanical illustration and knowledge four hundred years ago. Gesner was the first to show such enlargements.

It would be idle to speculate what the impact on botany would have been if Gesner had lived long enough to publish most of his pictures. Many were printed for the first time in the eighteenth century at Nuremberg by Schmiedel. Most of the originals have fortunately survived, some in the Felix Platter Herbarium at Basel, more in two of the three original volumes in the University Library of Erlangen. They are by no means even in quality, but many are remarkable for their realism, completeness, and beauty.

But even without the publication of most of his drawings, Gesner's influence on contemporary botany was immense. Not only the drawings, for which he employed a variety of artists, but also his vast botanical garden at Zürich were the product of his own lifelong studies in Switzerland and elsewhere, and his large correspondence and exchange of botanical specimens with people all over Europe, including several Englishmen, among them Turner and John Parkhurst, Bishop of Norwich. Gesner was the man in the sixteenth century who had the most comprehensive knowledge of European plants. And he always generously shared his knowledge with others. He was one of the first scientists in spirit, dedicated to the propagation of knowledge. Once when Leonhard Fuchs interceded with him not to proceed with the publication of his botanical work while Fuchs himself was planning his own, he gently protested that in the interest of truth both men should impart their knowledge to mankind, and neither should suppress it out of a squeamish feeling of courtesy toward the other.

Humanists, Zoologists, and Compilers. Like William Turner and Leonhard Fuchs, Konrad Gesner was a humanist, that is to say a member of an impressive movement of scholars who reacted against medieval philosophy and who were dedicated to the revival of classical learning. The humanists revered the civilizations of ancient Rome and Greece, particularly of Greece, and they regarded as primary authorities in most subjects of humane learning, including biology, the superior classical writers: in zoology, Aristotle and to some extent Pliny; in botany, Theophrastus and Dioscorides. The humanists saw it as one of their main tasks to establish the best possible texts of the classics by studying the earliest surviving manuscripts. In natural history they recognized the great superiority of Greek writers over Latin, unlike most students in the Middle Ages who were content with versions derived from Pliny or his later popularizer and compiler Solinus. They edited the Greek works in the original language – Aristotle was only known in Latin during the Middle Ages – and retranslated them into what they judged to be precise and good classical versus debauched, medieval Latin. In this enormous project they benefited from the coincidence of the invention of the printing press about 1450. Printed works could be reproduced far more rapidly and cheaply than manuscripts, and thus enjoy a relatively wide circulation. Many of the incunabula, that is to say books printed before 1500, were humanistic editions of classics, usually in folio. For instance, Aristotle's *Opera omnia*, or complete works, appeared in a new Latin translation by Lorenzo Valla at Padua, in 1472–74, and several times more before 1500. The famous printer-editor Aldus Manutius published a splendid edition of the Greek works of Aristotle plus the botanical treatises of Theophrastus at Venice in 1495–98. Another Greek edition prepared by the famous Erasmus of Rotterdam appeared in two volumes at Basel in 1531. But of Aristotle's works on animals, the *Historia animalium, De partibus, De motu, De incessu,* and *De generatione animalium,* the most influential work in the late fifteenth and sixteenth centuries became the Latin translations by Theodore Gaza, on which Turner, for instance, depended for his work on birds.

Similar attention was paid to the treatises of the other classical writers on natural history. Editions of Dioscorides were particularly numerous, of which we will mention here only the two most influential in the sixteenth century, one by Jean Ruel, 1516, often reprinted, and later (1544) the lavishly illustrated one by the Italian botanist Mattioli, with whom Gesner and Turner frequently corresponded. Mattioli's was much more than an edition of Dioscorides' text. His annotations are full of the knowledge that he and his contemporaries had assembled not only from other classical sources but also from studies in the field. His work appeared in more than sixty editions and was translated into several other languages. Some of the reprintings were especially gorgeous folios. The illustrations, which only appeared in the later editions, were provided by Giorgio Liberale of Udine. Unfortunately, Mattioli did not supervise the artist or the printer, so that sometimes the pictures appear at the wrong place. They bear comparison in quality with those of Kandel in Bock's herbal, but not with the great achievements of Weiditz or the artists employed by Fuchs. They are distinctive for their lavishness and sometimes their prettiness. In the later edition (1586) of Mattioli by Joachim Camerarius the Younger, many of the figures are replaced by superior ones whose source is Gesner. We have dwelt so long on this point of the humanistic editions because the reader should be aware that all the men whose names are mentioned in this survey had Aristotle, Theophrastus, Dioscorides, Pliny, and other Latin writers at their fingertips. Study of biology began with these writers, however much it might be expanded or qualified by observation in the field.

But did humanism have a salutary influence on the development of biology? Or did it merely replace the blind adherence to one tradition by the frenzied worship of another? How could the immense faith that humanist biologists had in Aristotle and other classical authorities in any way encourage in them the experimental spirit exemplified by field work? We have already noted that William Turner and Konrad Gesner, at least among mid-sixteenth-century botanists, were ardent students of plants in the field and were occasionally willing to "correct" Aristotle. But the questions of the interaction between humanism and scientific observation can more easily be studied in the zoologists of the period rather than the botanists, because zoology was less dominated by traditional medicine; in botany, humanistic motives were constantly obscured by utilitarian medical considerations. A negative consequence of this relative freedom of zoology, however, was that it took much longer to establish itself as a worthwhile science. Very few books devoted to animals or birds appeared during the first half of the sixteenth century. Then, from about 1550 on, the situation changed.

Of the mid-sixteenth-century books on animals by humanists, the least original is a Latin work by the Englishman Edward Wotton. The *De differentiis animalium* was printed at Paris in 1552 and dedicated to Edward VI. The work was inspired by two earlier sixteenth-century compendia or pandects, one by Ruel on plants, the other by Agricola on minerals. These writers had collated the information relevant to their subject from numerous classical and some medieval writers and arranged the results in an ordered system, a kind of collection of extracts from earlier authors with comment. Except for being more specialized, such works represent the Renaissance equivalent of the medieval encyclopedias. Wotton attempted to do for animals, birds, and fishes what Ruel and Agricola had done for plants and minerals. His work is an astonishing mosaic of extracts from every sort of Greek and Roman writer: not only Aristotle, Pliny, Dioscorides, Galen, and Aelian, but also some of the historians and poets, for instance Virgil and Ovid. Yet it is a small work by comparison with the encyclopedic survey of the different groups of animals by Konrad Gesner, whose five volumes were to appear within the next fifteen years, and the still larger work of Ulisse Aldrovandi, most of which was only published in the seventeenth century by his students in a long series of folios.

Wotton's work is divided into ten books or parts. The first three are devoted to the characteristics, functions, and differences of animals in general. Book IV deals with man; V, with "quadrupeds" that bear young, i.e., mammals; VI, with quadrupeds which lay eggs; VII, with birds; VIII, with fishes; IX, with insects; and X, with squids, crustaceans, and molluscs. The order is basically Aristotelian.

In general the work is an example of the humanistic writer on natural history who was completely fettered by classical authority derived from purely bookish learning. Wotton seems to have observed only very few of the species which he describes or about which he provides extracts from earlier authors. Usually he was interested not in an animal for its own sake, but only in what had been written about it. To C. E. Raven, "The result is a useful compendium of the traditional lore" (*English Naturalists*, 1947, p. 41). Even his contemporary, Konrad Gesner, wrote: "He teaches nothing new but gives a complete digest of previous works on the subject." Only a few times does Wotton reveal a healthy skepticism, an indication that he is not completely the slave of his humanistic bias. For instance, he questions the legend of the unique phoenix bird, a myth not only found in Pliny, Aelian, and thence in medieval bestiaries, but immensely popular in the literature of Tudor England. His independent knowledge is most in evidence in the ninth book, which is devoted to insects. Especially interesting there is his treatment of generation. Wotton questions the tradition that practically all insects are spontaneously generated. He grants it for caterpillars on cabbages, human lice, and a few others but knows that some insects are produced by parents. He is acquainted not only with certain beetles and moths, but also with their larvae. But these are the few exceptions in a work which is little else but a compendium of what earlier biologists, historians, and poets said about animals.

Though William Turner was reared as strongly in the humanistic tradition as Wotton, his little book on birds, *Avium praecipuarum, quarum apud Plinium et Aristotelem mentio est, brevis et succincta historia* (1544), is a very different kind of work. First of all, it is much more specialized than Wotton's book. It is in fact the very first of the long series of great studies by Englishmen that are entirely devoted to birds. Secondly, it is a more original book than Wotton's. Fortunately it is available in a modern edition, with translation (*Turner on Birds*, ed. A. H. Evans, 1903).

Similar in aim and method to his first two botanical works, the Latin *Libellus* of 1538 and *The Names of Herbs,* 1548, Turner's book on birds reflects clearly how a scholarly humanistic undertaking led to the beginnings of scientific study and independent observation in the field. Following in the footsteps of his teacher Longolius, Turner made a systematic attempt to identify correctly the species of birds described by Aristotle and Pliny, and early came to realize that proper definition can finally be secured only through direct field observation. The difficulties he faced were enormous, partly because Pliny and even Aristotle frequently do not provide a sufficiently detailed and precise account of the shapes, colors, and habitats of certain species, and partly because the birds that Turner studied in England and Germany were naturally often different from those southern species listed by Aristotle. But Turner persevered with remarkable tenacity and scholarly honesty. Sometimes, naturally, he misidentified a species absurdly, but usually his identifications were acute, often completely accurate. When he remained baffled by a description in Aristotle or Pliny, he either acknowledged his

40

puzzlement openly or provided no comment. He did not allow himself to make wild guesses.

For each species Turner sets out the names in Greek, Latin, English, and German, as he had done in his botanical books. Then he quotes the descriptions from Gaza's translation of Aristotle and from Pliny. Quite often he leaves it at that, but a number of times he adds notes from authors ancient and modern and, most interestingly, provides his own comments and identifications. Sometimes he reports where he has observed certain birds in the field: among them the common crane, spoonbill (which he calls white heron), bittern, and black tern (of which he describes the nest) – all of which he had observed in East Anglia. When he dwells on Pliny's *Merops,* which had been variously translated but by which Pliny almost certainly meant the bee-eater, a bird not encountered in northern Europe, Turner admits that he has never seen the bird and then proceeds to prove that at any rate it cannot be the green woodpecker, as some had asserted. Significantly, he omits the bat, which bestiaries and medieval encyclopedias and later Renaissance books included among birds. He does cite Pliny on the legendary phoenix, but without comment. Of the barnacle goose, he relates the fantastic folk belief in its spontaneous generation (see below, p. 47) and Giraldus Cambrensis' account in his *Topographia Hibernica* of *ca.* 1188 and adds:

But inasmuch as it seemed hardly safe to trust the vulgar and by reason of the rarity of the thing I did not quite credit Gyraldus, while I thought on this, of which I now am writing, I took counsel of a certain man, whose upright conduct, often proved by me, had justified my trust, a theologian by profession and an Irishman by birth, Octavian by name . . . . Who, taking oath upon the very Gospel which he taught, answered that what Gyraldus had reported of the generation of this bird was absolutely true, and that with his own eyes he had beholden young, as yet but rudely formed, and also handled them [Evans ed., p. 27].

Gesner in turn accepted this story from Turner. Though Turner in this case was deceived (as others have perhaps been since by

Irish theologians in matters of scientific accuracy), the story is nevertheless symptomatic of his enquiring yet skeptical scientific mind. He is of course far more prone to distrust stories from medieval writers or Pliny than from the great Aristotle whom he worshiped as a humanist, yet his bias toward the latter did not prevent him from occasionally discovering that even Aristotle was far from faultless. For instance, in the *Historia animalium* (ix. 256), Aristotle had suggested that the rubecula or robin changes in winter into a ruticilla or redstart. Turner knew better from observation in Germany or England: "All that Aristotle here has written of these two birds Pliny has copied from him into his own work. But in this matter each of them, relying on the tales of fowlers more than on his own experience, has wandered greatly from the path of truth. For both the birds are seen at the same time." Not every humanist-biologist of the sixteenth century was prepared occasionally to contrast his own observation in the field with the accounts of classical authorities. From the point of view of the development of ornithology, however, the most remarkable parts of Turner's bird book are his clear descriptions of living birds (even sometimes when he has erroneously identified Aristotle's Greek birds), their appearance, and some details of habitat and food. There had been nothing like this before by an Englishman, or for that matter by a European with the exception of Longolius. While the birds are presented in simple alphabetical order, suiting the humanistic purpose of the work, Turner appended a useful, broad classification according to physical characteristics, food, and habitat – an important beginning of real interest in this subject. The distinguished modern English ornithologist, James Fisher, thus estimates the measure of Turner's achievement: "If we remove from his 130 recognisable birds those which are domestic or were not seen in Britain, we are left with 105 species . . . of which no less than thirty-seven have appeared as British birds in no previous document, manuscript or printed, that I have seen or heard of" (*History of Birds*, 1954, p. 20). Of several families of birds, such as buntings, finches, and tits, Turner distinguished various species which previously had been designated as one and recorded his observations on their different habitats. In other instances, he identified as male and female of the same species birds that previously had been regarded as different species – for instance certain male and female hawks that differ considerably in color and color-pattern.

Like Turner, John Caius, after whom Caius College, Cambridge, has been named, had a basic humanistic education in England and then went south for more advanced medical training (see Plate 9). He became a student of no lesser a man than Vesalius, whose brilliant revolutionary work on anatomy appeared in 1543. After returning to England, Caius became lecturer on anatomy, first in London and then at Gonville and Caius College in Cambridge. There he instituted an annual public dissection. Only much later did he publish two very small biological studies, a treatise on English dogs, which was translated into English by Fleming in 1576, and the *De rariorum animalium atque stirpium historia* (London, 1570). Long before these books, however, several of Caius' descriptions and drawings of animals had appeared in Gesner's vast works, with due acknowledgment.

In view of his training under Vesalius and his introduction of modern anatomy to England, one might imagine that in his studies of plants and animals Caius would be even more liberal in his humanism, more independent of classical authority, than was William Turner. But the opposite is the case. Indeed Caius is perhaps the best example of a scientifically talented and enterprising Englishman of the sixteenth century whose observations were severely compromised by humanistic bias. Even in medicine he could be appallingly conservative. When a certain Oxford physician once claimed that Galen had made mistakes, Caius, then President of the Royal College of Physicians in London, insisted that unless he explicitly recanted he should be imprisoned as a charlatan. In zoological matters, his humanistic bias is in evidence in his description, accompanied by a drawing, of a young female elk: "In Norway they call it an elk or elend, but in this they are plainly mistaken; for it has not the legs of an elk since they never bend." Where did he get this curious idea

Plate 9. Portrait of John Caius in the College Hall, Caius College, Cambridge. (Reproduced from *The Works of John Caius, M.D.*, ed. E. S. Roberts [1912]).

from? From Julius Caesar, who in a passage in the *Gallic Wars* transferred from the elephant to the elk the traditional myth that its legs lack joints.

Though humanistic bias led Caius sometimes into grave mistakes, he nevertheless made a very real contribution to man's developing knowledge of species and exercised a considerable influence on his contemporaries and on later students of zoology. The *De rariorum animalium* contains accounts of several native birds, including the osprey, puffin, sea pie, and dotterel, of fishes, but above all of animals from Africa and other distant parts, some of which he had observed in the royal menagerie in the Tower of London. Of these, he made very capable drawings and descriptions, several of which were the first to be made by any European. They include a hunting leopard or cheetah from Mauretania, lynx, Getulan (Moroccan) hound, civet cat, Barbary sheep, hartebeest, Getulan squirrel, Barbary ape, marmoset, chameleon, guinea fowl, a Brazilian parrot (probably macaw), and others.

We would be able to appreciate the full extent of the investigations of animals by neither Turner nor Caius were it not for frequent acknowledgments to them in the five folio volumes devoted to animals by Konrad Gesner. Gesner also records the names of a number of other Englishmen, foremost among them John Parkhurst, Bishop of Norwich, a prominent reformer some of whose correspondence is extant in the "Zürich Letters"; of Parkhurst's activities in natural history there would otherwise be hardly a record.

Gesner (see Plate 2) was the greatest of the humanistic encyclopedists of zoology. Of his contribution to botany, we spoke earlier. In zoology, he set himself the task of composing, on a scale much larger than Wotton's, works on quadrupeds, fishes, reptiles, birds, and other animals. These works were to contain organized summaries of everything that had been written on the various species by classical zoologists, historians, poets, medical men, and mythographers, accompanied by woodcuts based on modern drawings of these animals. But as his study developed it became still more comprehensive and was brought up to date.

Each account of a species begins with a philological section listing the names by which the animal is known, not only in Greek and Latin, but also in a considerable number of modern languages and dialects. Gesner thereby satisfied his instinct as a linguist of extraordinary accomplishment. As he needed many hundreds of specimens or at least drawings for his artists to work on, he traveled far afield and engaged in an extensive correspondence with men all over Europe. The result is an enormous encyclopedia quite different in kind not merely from those of Bartholomaeus Anglicus and Neckam, but also from Wotton's. The classification of the animals is partly Aristotelian, partly alphabetical. Each animal is first represented in a picture. The text begins with some philological paragraphs on the animal's names. This is followed by a lengthy account of its appearance and other physical characteristics, its habitat, and food. That, however, is not the end; sections devoted to the animal's place in poetry and in hieroglyphics, its many moral applications, its medical uses, and so on, follow. Each section is packed with quotations from "authorities" whether classical or contemporary, poets, and scientists. A strange hodgepodge this, where scientific observations are mixed with lore. It is indicative of a period in the history of thought when the approach to truth through analytical investigation had begun but had not yet conquered traditional, more synthetic, and symbolic approaches. On the one hand, Gesner did incorporate in his huge work much "hearsay" from the past. On the other hand, he was eager in the pursuit of truth (in a more modern sense) to the extent of rejecting several of the more fantastic legends derived from Pliny or Aelian or medieval sources. He was not the slave of traditional superstitions or more modern impostures: he rejected outright the medical virtues widely attributed by dubious individuals on the market place to the unicorn's horn. If his work nevertheless includes much traditional lore, we can attribute it partly to Gesner's humanism, that is, the excessive respect he paid to classical authors, and partly to the very encyclopedic nature of the work. Yet this work is at the same time a remarkable record of the endeavor, by himself and hundreds of contemporary naturalists, to examine species firsthand in museums and, if possible, in the field.

Gesner's animal encyclopedias enjoyed tremendous prestige and popularity throughout Europe, including England, for the next hundred years. They were reprinted several times and soon translated into German. Early in the seventeenth century they were rivaled only by the very similar encyclopedias by the Bolognese Ulisse Aldrovandi, who however very largely copied Gesner's work. In England, Edward Topsell, Anglican priest and a contemporary of Shakespeare, endeavored to popularize Gesner among his countrymen through what is a very free translation, with adaptations and additions, of his work (see Plate 10). Topsell's two folios, *The History of Four-Footed Beasts* (1607) and *The History of Serpents* (1608) – in fact reptiles, amphibians, and other animals except for fishes and birds – and his projected third volume, which he was unable to publish, "The Fowls of Heaven" (*ca.* 1613; part of MS now in Huntington Library), all show no originality whatsoever in zoological matters. Topsell was neither scientific investigator nor humanist. He had barely enough Latin to translate Gesner, not without some appalling howlers. He did show initiative in turning to additional sources, including some of the drawings of John White, the artist who accompanied Thomas Hariot to Roanoke in 1585 (see Plates 17 and 18), and for the bird book to the *Ornithologiae* of Ulisse Aldrovandi which he summarized as slavishly as he did Gesner. A few times, Topsell's descriptions read like personal adventures with animals; in each case, however, scholars have shown that Topsell is in fact stealing from some other author. Temperamentally, he was anything but a pioneer, but he was fascinated by much of the lore of the past (see Plate 11) and even sometimes took issue with the healthy skepticism of his contemporaries. For instance, though he himself knew that the Dutch voyagers under De Veer had discovered barnacle geese nesting like other geese at Spitzbergen, he still stressed the old legendary accounts, derived from Giraldus Cambrensis, of barnacle geese spontaneously generating from driftwood or certain trees in the Orkney Islands and Hebrides. He arrived at the conclusion that some-

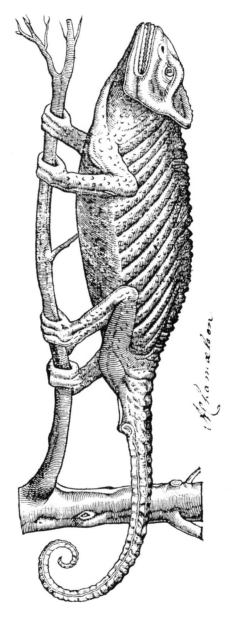

Plate 10. Chameleon. From Edward Topsell,
History of Serpents (1608).

times barnacle geese reproduce normally and sometimes by spontaneous generation.

His reason for clinging to such old beliefs was religious: barnacle geese reproducing by spontaneous generation would be a small miracle by comparison with God's creation of man and of all animal species. Topsell's ostensible aim in his animal books would have surprised (though not shocked) Gesner: to acquaint his readers with all the animals referred to in Scripture; for neither, says Topsell, can we understand Scripture properly without knowing the animals or birds there referred to nor can we understand the true significance of these animals without Scripture. This theological motive, however, is lost sight of in large parts of his books, for these are after all straight translations or summaries from Gesner and Aldrovandi. The fantastic inclusiveness of treatment in Topsell is due to his sources, an inclusiveness that goes far beyond the creatures mentioned in the Bible. And the title page of "The Fowls of Heaven" shows that the various sections of his treatment correspond to those in Gesner or Aldrovandi: "History of birds containing their true and lively figures with the whole description of their natures in readings grammatical, logical, philosophical, theological, hieroglyphical, medicinal and civil . . . ." In the continuation of this booklet, it will be shown how an equally religious Englishman, John Ray, was to react against such an attempt, derived from Gesner, to surround the real matter of natural history with all sorts of "humane" but, to the subject matter, irrelevant learning. While, as we have seen, humanism sometimes gave an impetus to scientific investigation in natural history, it tended to encumber it with large amounts of grammar, philology, classical quotations, citations from emblem books, medical lore, and so on, which obscured the advance of genuine nature study.

This account of sixteenth-century zoology would be incomplete without a mention of a figure frequently cited by Gesner and thus Topsell, the French biologist Pierre Belon. That man occupies a unique place in the history of biology of his time because his work contains very few humanistic preoccupations. In his main zoological work, *Histoire de la nature des oiseaux,*

Plate 11. Mantichora. From Edward Topsell, *History of Four-Footed Beasts* (1607).

his approach is direct and unpedantic. Unlike Gesner, he usually ignores the lore of the past, though he does deal with the phoenix, misidentifying it as one of the East Indian birds of paradise; here he apposes an illustration of the "true" phoenix to one of the "legendary" phoenix (see Plates 12 and 13). One of Belon's most remarkable innovations is the classification of birds according to habitat: diurnal and nocturnal birds of prey, water birds of marsh and shore, and birds of wood and field, large and small – the latter divided into worm- and seedeaters. Such an attempt at classification was almost unique at the time. Further, Belon was the first to devote a whole chapter to the importance of anatomy in bird study, an interest which was later developed by Aldrovandi. But Belon's fame rests above all on his juxtaposition, as a demonstration in comparative anatomy, of skeletal drawings of a man and a bird, for which he derived his inspiration no doubt from Vesalius. Yet only a very few people in England seem to have been acquainted with the work of this man, who was perhaps the most modern-minded among the biologists of the sixteenth century.

The Flemish Botanists, Lyte, and Thomas Penny. After this survey of sixteenth-century zoology, we return to botany. Earlier in the century, as we have shown, several Germans were particularly prominent in botany. But this position of dominance was taken over later in the century by a trio of Flemish botanists, Rembert Dodoens or Dodonaeus, Charles de l'Écluse or Clusius, and Matthias de l'Obel or Lobelius. The influence of the second of these, Clusius, on the development of English botany was indirect and relatively small. Dodoens is closely linked, as we will see, with the two herbals which succeeded Turner's in England, Lyte's herbal and Gerard's. But of the three Lobelius is the most important, because he did much of his work in England and had an original mind.

Henry Lyte's *A New Herbal or History of Plants,* published at Antwerp in 1578, was a translation of the improved French adaptation of Dodoens' *Cruydeboeck,* which Clusius had edited

*Tant hault en l'air ie me pais de rosée,
Qu'impossible est me pouuoir vif auoir,
Ny mesmement qu'apres ma mort me voir.
Voila comment ma vie est composée.*

Plate 12. Paradise bird, interpreted as "true phoenix."
From Pierre Belon, *Portraits d'oiseaux* (1557). (Courtesy of the Newberry Library.)

Le Phœnix selon que le vulgaire a coustume de le portraire.

O du Phœnix la diuine excellence!
Ayant vescu seul sept cens soixante ans,
Il meurt dessus des ramées d'ancens :
Et de sa cendre vn autre prend naissance.

Plate 13. Phoenix (traditional). From Pierre Belon, *Portraits d'oiseaux* (1557), in which it faces the picture shown on the previous plate. (Courtesy of the Newberry Library.)

in 1557. Dodoens' work had been a herbal of rather traditional kind by a medical man. He depended mainly on the ancient and contemporary literature on botany, but he was also well acquainted with the herbaria of Flanders. The basic arrangement of his plants is almost fortuitous, with little indication of any taxonomical interest, but he does provide a clear and objective, if rather brief, orderly account, giving a chapter to each species or group of closely related species and dividing it by means of the subheadings so familiar in herbals: place, time, names, nature, and medical uses. From time to time, he includes an old legend from the classics, for instance the story of Narcissus.

Henry Lyte, the translator of Dodoens, was not a naturalist himself but an educated country gentleman with a genuine interest in nature. He added to the work a number of personal notes, a few of which, but only a few, record his own amateur observations of plants in his native western England. More often, the additions are derived from Turner's herbal or from Cooper's *Thesaurus* of 1578, a famous dictionary which included many of the native names of plants, largely derived from Turner. Unfortunately it is often difficult to be sure about Lyte's additions, for some of them are set off in the dominantly black letter text by Roman type but others are not. Whenever in Lyte's herbal the location of a plant is given as "in this country," we can be sure that Flanders is meant.

Lyte's herbal is thus a much less original work than was Turner's. Yet his translation became deservedly popular. The plants are more attractively arranged than in Turner, and Lyte was fortunate in procuring many additional woodcuts based on the brilliant pictures in Fuchs. Of his 1,050 plants, over 800 are illustrated. Scholars have convincingly argued that if Shakespeare was familiar with any specific herbal it was Lyte's. There he could read about the use of mandragora as an anesthetic, an observation derived from Dioscorides (*Antony and Cleopatra* I.v.4–5); about the "cursed hebenon" which Claudius poured into Hamlet Senior's ear, and by which probably henbane is meant (*Hamlet* I.v.61–64); about the bitter-tasting coloquintida (*Othello* I.iii.355–56); about the mountain cedar which spreads "his branches / To all the plains about him" (*Henry VIII* V.v.54–55); and about such southern vegetation as the "soft myrtle" (*Measure for Measure* II.ii.117), soft because it is difficult to keep in a northern climate. Lyte's herbal was several times reprinted and deservedly the most popular herbal in England during the last two decades of the sixteenth century. Then it was replaced by Gerard's herbal, likewise indebted to Dodoens, but this will be reserved for later treatment.

Far more influential in the development of English botany than Dodoens was his younger countryman, Matthias de l'Obel or Lobelius. Lobelius came to England first in or about 1567 as a Protestant refugee from southern France and in the company of a French fellow botanist, Pierre Pena. They lived for some time in London and in Somerset near Bristol at the house of Lobelius' patron, Edward St. Loo. Together with Pena, Lobelius published in 1570–71, in London, a remarkable illustrated botanical treatise with the unassuming title of *Stirpium adversaria nova* or "New Memoranda on Plants." Pena soon after its publication returned to France, there to become private physician to Henry III, and made, as far as is known, no further important contribution to botany. Lobelius too returned to the Continent about 1574 but eventually resettled in England in 1586 and, except for brief trips abroad, remained there for the rest of his life. We shall relate later (in the companion booklet) how in the 1590's he became first a close friend of Gerard's, the author of the famous herbal, and later quarreled with him. Lobelius was by then attached to the household of Edward Baron Zouche, whom he accompanied on a mission to Denmark, where he did a considerable amount of botanizing, the results of which he published in an appendix to the 1605 edition of the *Adversaria* and in the *Stirpium illustrationes*. On Zouche's estate at Hackney, he developed a famous physic garden. Toward the end of his life, he was at work on another ambitious botanical project, the *Stirpium illustrationes*. After his death in 1616, the manuscript of this work passed by purchase into the hands of John Parkinson who used it for his *Theatrum botanicum* (1640). Still later, in 1655, part of the manuscript itself was published by William How who violently but unjustly charged Parkinson with plagiarism. The manuscript is now in the library of Magdalen College, Oxford. Lobelius may well have died unhappily, for his son had become involved in the scandal and trial which followed Sir Thomas Overbury's murder at the Tower in 1613.

The very presence in England of a foreign botanist of Lobelius' prestige ensured continued contact between the main naturalists of England and of the Continent. Even if he had published no books, his impact on English botany would have been immense. This account, however, will confine itself almost completely to his first work. For simplicity's sake, it will be discussed as his alone though for all we know Pena may have had a major share in it.

The *Adversaria* presents an excellent survey of the flora of the Montpellier region, and its Preface is suitably addressed to the professors of the University of Montpellier where both Lobelius and Pena had studied under Rondelet until 1566, the year of the latter's death. The authors were able to publish the book in England several years after leaving France simply because they brought their plants with them. Yet in several ways they added to their work, thus making it more relevant to the English scene. They dedicated it to Queen Elizabeth, expressing in their dedication their appreciation of English hospitality and providing a list of their English medical and botanical friends. In this list, the foremost place is given to William Turner as a great doctor and writer of herbals. Among the other names, we find that of Caius. But finally they single out a certain Thomas Penny – *magnaeque spei & peritiae in hac parte D. Thomae Pennio* (see Plate 16). In fact they had met Penny, about whom more will be said in this survey, as a fellow student at Montpellier. Later in the work, in the section devoted to "Aconitum pardalianches," he is described as "our friend of many conversations and excursions, the very learned doctor Pennius Anglus." But it is not merely the Dedication and the place of publication that link the work to England. By 1570 Pena and Lobelius had amassed a great number of plants in England, either indigenous or from abroad, which incidentally included one species of American tobacco, *Nicotiana tabacum,* of

which they provided the first printed illustration (Plate 15).
While the book is devoted to the plants of the Montpellier
region, they frequently mention that they also encountered a
plant in England or were furnished with a specimen by one of
their English friends.

The work's major claim to importance, however, is that it
includes the first serious attempt in European botany at discovering a unified order in the plant kingdom and at devising a system
of plant classification based mainly on differences of leaf form.
Nothing like it is intimated in Turner's herbal. The system was to
be superseded only by Gaspar Bauhin in 1626. According to the
Preface the idea for this classification was inspired by Theophrastus. Translating freely from Lobelius and Pena, we read:
As there is nothing more beautiful than the order of the skies or
of the soul of wisdom itself, so we should aim at discovering the
laws of order in nature herself. If we discover a unified order in
the plant kingdom, then it will appear that "things which are far
and widely different become, as it were, one thing." Accordingly,
in the work itself each "genus" or natural group of plants is
headed by a synoptic table of its various species; for instance on
page 1:

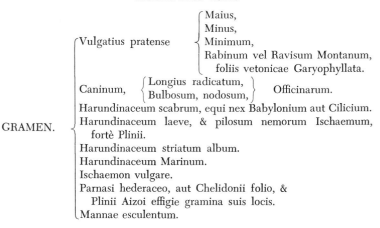

Gramnis omne Genus

GRAMEN.
{
Vulgatius pratense {
Maius,
Minus,
Minimum,
Rabinum vel Ravisum Montanum,
foliis vetonicae Garyophyllata.

Caninum, { Longius radicatum, / Bulbosum, nodosum, } Officinarum.
Harundinaceum scabrum, equi nex Babylonium aut Cilicium.
Harundinaceum laeve, & pilosum nemorum Ischaemum,
fortè Plinii.
Harundinaceum striatum album.
Harundinaceum Marinum.
Ischaemon vulgare.
Parnasi hederaceo, aut Chelidonii folio, &
Plinii Aizoi effigie gramina suis locis.
Mannae esculentum.

While a modern botanist would find much to question and
even to reject in the work's arrangement, what matters is that we

Hyoſcyamus luteus. Yellowe Henbane.

Plate 14. The earliest picture of a tobacco plant, *Nicotiana rustica*, called "yellow henbane." First appeared in Rembert Dodoens, *Cruydeboeck* (1554). From Henry Lyte's translation, *A New Herbal, or History of Plants* (1578).

Nicotiana
inſerta in-
fundibulo
ex quo hau-
riunt fumũ
Indi & nau
cleri.

Plate 15. The first picture of a tobacco plant, *Nicotiana tabacum,* in an English book. From Matthias de l'Obel and Pierre Pena, *Stirpium adversaria nova* ("New Memoranda on Plants") (1570–71).

have here the first major attempt at systematically classifying and thereby discovering a unified order in the plant kingdom. Moreover their emphasis on foliar characteristics was basically sound. Lobelius' fellow countryman Dodoens had attempted as early as 1554 a general scheme of classification, but without any guiding principle, attaching little or no importance to the structure of the flowers and fruits and to the shape of leaves. But Lobelius with his seeing eye distinguished the two classes of plants known in modern botany as monocotyledons and dicotyledons. The superiority of Lobelius' classification was recognized by the great Antwerp printer of herbals Plantin, who applied it to a reissue of Dodoens' *Plantarum seu stirpium icones* in 1581. In England, however, no botanical work was to equal Lobelius' own in this respect before the great works of Ray and Grew near the end of the seventeenth century.

Most of the works by the three great Flemish botanists (though not Dodoens' Flemish herbal) were produced by Plantin. From 1566 on, Plantin employed artists who prepared the drawings for the illustrations in his botanical publications, among whom the greatest was Pieter van der Borcht. In 1581, he also purchased the woodblocks which had been used by Jean van der Loe for Dodoens' *Cruydeboeck*. Gradually Plantin thus assembled a vast collection of botanical woodblocks which were used for the books by Dodoens, Lobelius, and Clusius. The collection became understandably popular, and many of the pictures are closely copied in the works of British and other European botanists, including Gerard, Jean Bauhin, and Parkinson. Of the woodcuts, some of the best illustrate the work of Clusius, who often included fruiting as well as flowering stages of the species he described. By comparison with those in Fuchs and even Brunfels, however, the Plantin illustrations have one major drawback: their small size. For reasons of economy, Plantin vetoed folio-size illustrations, so that the pictures in the Flemish herbals are sometimes lacking in clarity and detail. Of Clusius' original plant drawings in water color, 1,856 have survived in the Preussische Staatsbibliothek of Berlin. They were executed under his direction, many of them by Van der Borcht.

The three great Flemish botanists, however, did not benefit from a major technical development in the art of book illustration which began late in the sixteenth century: the replacement of woodcuts by copper engraving. Engraving in metal allowed for more realistic presentation of minute detail and was therefore to be of immense benefit in the development of botanical science. The first botanical copper engravings are found in the Φυτοβασανος (or *Phytobasanos*) of 1592 by Fabio Colonna, the etchings in which work are remarkable for their accuracy of detail and for their design. The *Phytobasanos*, incidentally, is the first work which provides proof by way of illustration that barnacles are entirely unrelated to young barnacle geese. Two decades later, a superior Dutch artist, Crispijn van de Passe the Younger, provided many large quarto-size engravings of several species of tulip and other flowers in his *Hortus floridus* of 1614, an English edition of which work, entitled *A Garden of Flowers*, was published at Utrecht in 1615. The artist capitalized on the new craze for tulips in his native country. The book did not so much add to man's botanical knowledge as to his appreciation of the beauty of flowers, by showing them from so low a level that the plants stand up against the sky. It is still a treasured collector's item.

Among the many English botanists whom Lobelius counted among his friends, the greatest was probably Thomas Penny, whom he first met at Montpellier and again after Lobelius came to England in 1567. The tribute which Lobelius pays to Penny in the Dedication to his *Adversaria* has already been cited. However, while Lobelius' contributions to botany can easily be assessed from his books and manuscripts, Thomas Penny's eminence in this field can only be derived indirectly from the many references to him in the works of others, for he never published a single book. Born in northern England about 1530 he became, like Turner and Caius, a student at Cambridge, first at Queen's College, later at Trinity. At Trinity he was elected Fellow in 1553, and he became its Senior Bursar in 1564. Meanwhile he had been ordained deacon at Ely in 1561. He gave the Spital Sermon at Paul's Cross on Easter Sunday, 1565. However, as he was decidedly Puritan in his leanings, he was criticized by Archbishop Parker and ran into difficulties. It was perhaps already then that he decided to become a "layman," for he turned his main attention to medicine, botany, and entomology, though he was formally deprived of his prebend only in 1577. Later in 1565 Penny visited Gesner in Zürich and thence went to Geneva. There is record of his botanizing in the Jura and the Savoy, where he provided many notes on the localities of orchids and gentians. After some months at Geneva, he first returned to Zürich to help Gesner's executors, Kaspar Wolf and Jean Bauhin, with sorting out Gesner's vast materials toward a general history of plants. When most of these were at last published two centuries later, C. C. Schmiedel, the editor, reports in his "Historia operis" to the second volume, probably following notes by Wolf, that Penny "passed over but a few of the sheets of pictures without adding some observations and notes, particularly about localities." Indeed, thirty-three such notes can be identified in Schmiedel's work, and some of the Gesner originals with Penny's annotations have fortunately survived until this day in the library of the University of Erlangen.

It was probably a few months after this that Penny went to Montpellier and made the acquaintance of Lobelius. After a brief trip to Majorca, he was next at Orléans and Paris. By 1569 he was in Heidelberg, where he met Joachim Camerarius, a famous humanist and botanist of stature, in whose later *Hortus medicus* (1588) a number of plants brought to his attention by Penny are mentioned. Penny then went through Prussia to the Baltic, where he made one of his most famous discoveries of plants, the *Chamaepericlymenum* (*Cornus suecica*), which he gave to Clusius. He returned to England later in 1569 with his M.D. degree and after some difficulties settled there as an eminent doctor. It was probably then that he renewed his friendship with Lobelius. Later he entertained a visit from Clusius. He went on several botanizing expeditions to different parts of England but devoted the last years of his life mainly to insects, on which he evidently planned to publish a large work. Penny died in 1588. The record of his insect studies is found in Thomas Moffet's *Insectorum . . . theatrum* (1634), which work will be discussed in the companion booklet.

Many were the books of the time which included some drawings and descriptions of plants by Thomas Penny (see Plate 16). Though the descriptions were usually adapted by the various authors to fit their own text, one can fortunately in a few instances infer safely that the author took over Penny's very wording. These samples, if we can trust them perfectly, convey evidence of Penny's remarkable command of vivid, concise, and precise phrasing, in which technical terms are always employed accurately and the chief points of any species are conveyed with a clarity rarely equaled by any of Penny's contemporaries in botany. C. E. Raven provides the following translation from Clusius' *Stirpium pannonicarum historia* as a sample of Penny's style. It is a description of *Rubus chamaemorus*, which Penny saw in northern England, perhaps even before he went to Cambridge, and of which he sent Clusius an admirable picture and this "history":

Among thornless brambles we must include this elegant plant whose picture and history were communicated to us by the eminent Thomas Penny . . . under the title of Chamaemorus. It consists of stems twelve inches long on which alternately grow three, four or rarely five leaves, rough in texture, not unlike those of a mallow or rather a mulberry . . . divided into five points and serrated . . . on long pedicels, and springing out of two wings or processes . . . embracing the stalk. The top of the stem bears a single flower, standing out of blackish purple bracts. The fruit is very like that of a mulberry . . . (hence the name "ground-mulberry") but a little smaller, at first whitish and bitter, then red and sharply sweet. The root is knotted, sending out a few fibres from each knot. It spreads wonderfully and creeps very far, so that it quickly covers a wide area. It flowers in June and early July: the fruit is ripe in August. It loves snowy and open places and the tops of hills, and grows in great plenty among heather on mount Ingleborrow the highest in all England, twelve miles from Lancaster. The English call it knotberries from the knot-like fruit: to the taste it is astringent, drying and cooling [C. E. Raven, *English Naturalists from Neckam to Ray* (Cambridge: Cambridge University Press, 1947), p. 154].

Even a modern botanist will admire the preciseness and charm of this description. By comparison, that of the same plant in

Plate 16. Cyperus graminea. Drawn
by Thomas Penny. From Matthias de
l'Obel and Pierre Pena, *Stirpium
adversaria nova* (1570–71).

Gerard's *Herbal*, supplied by one Thomas Hesketh, is crude and defective.

The Voyagers: Flora and Fauna from Other Continents. Several times in the course of this survey we have already referred to animals and plants that were introduced to Europe from other continents during the sixteenth century. Caius described and made drawings which he sent to Gesner of several African mammals he had seen in the royal menagerie in London. A picture of the tobacco plant from America appears in Pena and Lobelius' *Adversaria* (see Plate 15). Several pictures in Topsell and in Moffet's *Insectorum . . . theatrum* (1634) are based on water colors by John White, painter, surveyor, and cartographer under the direction of Thomas Hariot during the Roanoke voyage of 1585–86. The extant originals of White's water colors of Indians and their way of living and of various animals and birds he encountered in Virginia and North Carolina are reproduced in the recently published and magnificently illustrated catalogue by David B. Quinn and P. H. Hulton from two portfolios in the British Museum. Topsell's debased copies of several of White's North American birds, including the towhee, eastern bluebird, flicker, blue jay, grackle, redwing blackbird, oriole, loon, and sandhill crane (see Plates 17 and 18), have also been reproduced recently in color and juxtaposed with White's originals in a charming little book edited by Thomas P. Harrison. Moffet derived from White a picture of a gadfly from Virginia and one of a species of Pyrophorus or firefly (see treatment of Moffet in the companion booklet, *The Growth of Natural History in Stuart England*).

It would be impossible to assess precisely the extent to which the voyagers of the fifteenth and sixteenth centuries and their discoveries of distant parts of the globe contributed to the development of man's knowledge of natural history. But it is certain that they contributed in several ways. At first this was perhaps mainly because of the attractiveness which the unfamiliar or extraordinary has for man. Travelers to Africa or America were

Plate 17. Sandhill crane. Water color by John White in the Sloane Collection, British Museum. (Reproduced from Hulton and Quinn, *The American Drawings of John White, 1577–1590* [1964], courtesy of the University of North Carolina Press).

Plate 18. Sandhill crane. Water color in Edward Topsell, "The Fowls of Heaven" (*ca.* 1613), Ellesmere MS 1142. (Courtesy of the Henry E. Huntington Library.)

struck by the behavior of certain animals that they had never encountered before and upon returning to their homeland inquired whether creatures like them had ever been known to Europeans – which in turn stimulated examination of local fauna. For instance, Peter Martyr, councilor to the king of Spain who accompanied Columbus to the West Indies, describes in some detail the fascination with which the explorers watched pelicans. His descriptions reappear in several later sixteenth-century sources, including Aldrovandi's *Ornithologiae* from which Topsell translated them for his "Fowls of Heaven":

Peter Martyr and Ramusius affirm that they have seen taken out of one of their throats a soldier's coat, a hat and three pair of shoes, which is no incredible thing, as we shall manifest when we come to their feeding. . . . As kites and other birds of prey fly high with a croaking voice above the waters looking earnestly downward when the fishes appear on the brinks or upper face of the waters, then suddenly they fall down like a great many hounds after one hare or boys to scramble for one muss, whereby the astonished fish becometh a prey without stirring: for their number and weight parteth the waters and openeth them the length of half an arm. Therefore saith Ramusius, they follow the skulls of herrings and take of them abundantly because they swim aloft and in great troops. First they prepare them in their prolobe or throat bag, then after a while they vomit them forth into their mouth and take them into their throat where they lie till they be half digested, then they let them sink down into their maw where the first concoction is perfected, which is very speedy because it is narrow and long, and . . . their bellies want room to retain their meat long. And it is a wonderful work of Almighty God that hath so made the bag of this fowl to retain at one time water, sand, stones, chips, fishes, and whatsoever else they devour, and yet none of these annoy the throat itself and passage to the maw, being so nearly conjoined as is the entry of a house unto the open hall; without muscle, vein or sinew to keep the passage for the natural foods either to open or shut the same. But like a bladder wideneth and contracteth of itself, according to the fullness and emptiness wherewithal it is charged: being made of a double thick skin full of fibers transparent and yet very strong, whereby it is dilated and contracted, and so when they have filled it, they feed upon the best as hath been declared, and the residue of any burden they cast up from being a trouble unto them. . . .

The voice of this bird is like the braying of an ass, for when she will make a noise she pitcheth her beak in the water or in the earth and roareth like a horn winded by a weak breath or one that hath no skill [Topsell, "The Fowls of Heaven," folios 23v, 24v–25r, 26r, courtesy of the Henry E. Huntington Library].

If possible, the voyagers would bring back with them live specimens of unusual animals or birds they encountered, or have artists draw them on the spot. Thus pictures of a fair variety of animals from other continents are included in Gesner's encyclopedic works on zoology. A quite impressive woodcut of the Central and South American armadillo, encountered to this day in Texas, is found in *Joyful News Out of the New Found World* (1577), a translation by John Frampton from a Spanish work of Nicolás Monardes (see Plate 19). Topsell's projected bird book contains a beautiful water color of a Japanese crane. The first known picture of the North American Hudsonian curlew was published by Clusius in 1605. Frequently, however, the voyagers and their accompanying biologists had to content themselves with bringing back the dried skins of animals. Thus it happens, for instance, that Aldrovandi's ornithological volumes, and hence Topsell's manuscript "The Fowls of Heaven," include several pictures and descriptions of Indonesian species of paradise birds, none of which is true to life because Aldrovandi and his artist had only skins to study.

American, African, or Asiatic plants would come to men's attention because of their sheer beauty, their medical uses, or because of their food value, and in one instance their source of a new pleasure – smoking. Indeed smoking was not known in Europe until the discovery of Indians smoking in various parts of America – about which more below. The main food plant introduced to Europe in the second half of the sixteenth century was another plant grown by the Indians in America, the potato, the first illustration of which in an English book is found in Gerard's *Herbal* of 1597 (Plate 20). Gerard calls the plant *Battata Virginiana sive Virginiaorum, et pappus,* "potatoes of Virginia," but the plant, first introduced in England by Drake in 1586, certainly came originally from South America. As the craze for elaborate

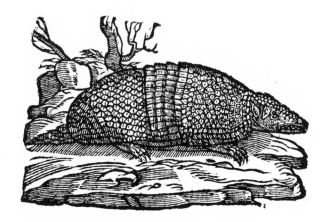

Plate 19. Armadillo. From Frampton's translation of Nicolás Monardes, *Joyful News* (1577).

Plate 20. Portrait of John Gerard holding a potato. Frontispiece in Gerard, *Herbal* (1597).

gardens developed among Renaissance gentlemen, the demand increased for exotic flowers from distant parts. The most famous of these undoubtedly was the tulip, which shortly after being introduced around 1600 to Holland from Turkey by Clusius caused in that country an almost incredible vogue of "tulipomania." But the tulip provides merely the most extreme example of how wealthy noblemen would outstrive one another for specimens of plants introduced from distant parts of the world for their gardens. For instance, the Folger Library has an original letter by Robert Dudley, Earl of Leicester, in which he urges Jean Hotman, Sieur de Villiers Saint Paul, to attempt to procure for him from Italy seeds "as well for herbs and salads as for all kind of rare flowers besides, seeds for melons, cauliflower and such like as asparagus and all sorts of radish" (Folger MS V.b.282). As gardens came to assume an important place in the splendor of Elizabethan aristocratic estates, some of the leading botanists were appointed to lucrative positions as official gardeners. Gerard, of whose *Herbal* there is a fuller treatment in the companion booklet, not only had his own garden but also looked after Lord Burghley's gardens in the Strand and at Theobalds in Hertfordshire. Lobelius, whose patron was Lord Zouche, was later appointed Regius Botanicus to King James I. So the leading botanists received every encouragement to introduce and study unusual flowering plants from Europe and other continents, and artists were employed to further advertise some of the most splendid acquisitions.

The fascinating story of how Europeans first encountered tobacco and how subspecies of the plant were gradually introduced into one European country after another is told by Jerome E. Brooks in the first volume of the brilliant printed catalogue of the Arents Collection of the New York Public Library.

The discoverers of the various parts of the American continent from Columbus on were startled when they came upon Indians smoking or chewing tobacco. The earliest printed reference to "the strange custom of chewing tobacco" relates Vespucci's experience and is found in Martin Waldseemueller's *Cosmographiae introductio* of 1507, but from about the same time comes Bartolomé de las Casas' enlargement of Columbus' own journal, though this was published only in 1875 as *Historia de las Indias*. It relates Columbus' encounter with smoking Indians in 1492, with snuff taking in 1494, and tobacco chewing in South America in 1502. There is an old story, though unverifiable, that Hernando Cortes, the conqueror of Mexico, presented tobacco grain to the Emperor Charles V in 1518. Jacques Cartier, who sailed up the St. Lawrence in 1535 as far as Hochelaga (Montreal) describes pipe-smoking Indians in his *Brief récit et succincte narration de la navigation faite aux isles de Canada* (1545). Cartier's account first appears in English, in somewhat garbled version, in Thomas Hacket's translation of A. Thevet, *The Newfound World, or Antarctic* (1568); again, rather differently, in John Frampton's translation of Nicolás Monardes, *Joyful News Out of the New Found World* (1577); and finally, accurately, in John Florio's translation of the Italian version by Ramusio, *A Short and Brief Narration of . . . New France* (1580). According to Florio's version, "They [the Canadian Indians] say that this [tobacco] doth keep them warm and in health; they never go without some of it about them. We ourselves have tried the same smoke, and having put it in our mouths, it seemed that they had filled it with pepper dust, it is so hot." As a final example, John Sparke the Younger reported how startled Hawkins was to encounter Indians smoking on his second voyage to Florida in 1564–65. The account which first appeared in Hawkins' *A True Declaration* (1569) is the first printed reference by an Englishman to tobacco, though the first reference in English occurs in Hacket's translation of Thevet a year earlier.

Some of Hawkins' sailors may have brought a specimen of the plant to England. At any rate, Pena and Lobelius in *Adversaria* (1570–71) refer to it as growing in England, and so does Harrison three years later. This indeed would be considerably later than on the Continent, for we know that Thevet introduced the southern variety of tobacco, *Nicotiana tabacum,* into France from Brazil in 1557 and that the more northern variety, *Nicotiana rustica,* arrived from Florida in Lisbon in 1560, from where Jean Nicot soon after sent it to France. How rapidly the tobacco craze developed in England we can gather from Thomas Hariot's *Brief and True Report . . . of Virginia* (1588), which alludes not merely to the plant's importation to England, but also to Elizabethan ladies of high estate indulging in pipe smoking.

The first illustration of a tobacco plant, *Nicotiana rustica,* is found in Dodoens' early Dutch herbal, the *Cruydeboeck* of 1554. He first misidentified it as a yellow variety of henbane, ascribing it to Peru only in 1574. The same picture was naturally reproduced by Lyte in his translation of 1578 (see Plate 14). The first picture in an English book, however, is that of *Nicotiana tabacum* in Pena and Lobelius' *Stirpium adversaria nova* (see Plate 15). They evidently brought a drawing of the plant with them from France. Their account conveys an idea of the enormous prestige, medical and otherwise, which tobacco had acquired by that time:

It is usually larger than our comfrey, though found flourishing in the same well-watered spots of rich earth, exposed to the sun. It has very wide leaves, of oblong shape, hairy quality, wider, rounder, larger than those of comfrey. . . . The stalk grows three cubits high in France, Belgium and England, and very often four or five cubits when it is sown early enough in warmer parts of Aquitaine and Languedoc. It bears flower calyxes in August of a pale, somewhat reddish green . . . . For you will observe shipmasters [sailors] and all others who come back from out there [i.e., America] using little funnels, made of palm leaves or straw, in the extreme end of which they stuff [crumbled dried leaves] of this plant. This they light, and opening their mouths as much as they can, they suck in the smoke with their breath. By this they say their hunger and thirst are allayed, their strength restored, and their spirits refreshed. . . . Our age has discovered nothing from the New World which will be numbered among the remedies more valuable and efficacious than this plant for sores, wounds, affections of the throat and chest, and the fever of the plague [Brooks' translation in *Tobacco,* I (New York: Rosenbach Company, 1937), pp. 239–40. This volume is a part of the Arents Collection, The New York Public Library].

Such an extraordinary claim for the medical benefits of tobacco was common in the late sixteenth century. Evidently no one then dreamed of a connection between smoking and lung cancer.

To conclude, this booklet has shown a considerable development in the scientific approach to botanical and zoological phenomena during the sixteenth century, both on the Continent and in Tudor England. At the same time, in literary and popular circles there was a strong persistence of the medieval tradition and of a dominating interest in the extraordinary and fantastical, as well as the moral, rather than in direct observation of natural phenomena. The subservience of botany to medicine remained strong though it was beginning to be challenged. And humanism sometimes merely substituted blind obedience to classical authority for medieval traditionalism, though often it directly encouraged a more critical approach which led to the beginnings of scientific investigation in modern Europe. How this scientific spirit in biology underwent a considerable further growth during the seventeenth century is told in the companion booklet: *The Growth of Natural History in Stuart England: From Gerard to the Royal Society.*

SUGGESTED READING

BY far the most thorough and comprehensive treatment of our subject is found in Canon Charles E. Raven, *English Naturalists from Neckam to Ray* (Cambridge, 1947). Though confining itself strictly to Englishmen, this eminently readable work has done much to correct the traditional underestimate of the advances in botany and zoology during the sixteenth and seventeenth centuries. On the other hand, L. C. Miall's *The Early Naturalists, Their Lives and Work* (*1530–1789*) (London, 1912) is disappointingly slight on the biologists before the Royal Society. *Shakespeare's England* (2 vols.; Oxford, 1916) contains brief but useful surveys on natural history (Vol. I, chap. xv) by C. T. Onions and Sir William T. Thiselton-Dyer. The development of biology during the sixteenth century, mainly on the Continent, is briefly treated in chapter ten of the first volume of W. P. D. Wightman, *Science and the Renaissance* (2 vols.; Edinburgh and London, 1962). There is no monograph in English on European zoology in the sixteenth century. The subject is broadly treated in Paul Delaunay, *La Zoologie au seizième siècle* (Paris, 1962).

Agnes Arber's *Herbals, Their Origin and Evolution . . . 1470–1670* (2d ed.; Cambridge, 1938, 1953) is the most scholarly and comprehensive treatment of Continental as well as English herbals of the period. Eleanour S. Rohde's *The Old English Herbals* (London, 1922) appeals to a more popular audience. The book covers a larger period than Arber's but confines itself to England. Edward Lee Greene's *Landmarks of Botanical History* (Washington, D.C., 1909), on the other hand, dwells mainly on Theophrastus and sixteenth-century German botanists. The artistry of the botanical woodcuts in our period is well discussed in Wilfred J. W. Blunt, *The Art of Botanical Illustration* (London, 1950). But the two most learned books on illustrations are the German ones by Claus Nissen: *Die botanische Buchillustration* (Stuttgart, 1951); and a similar work on birds, *Die illustrierten Vogelbücher* (Stuttgart, 1953).

A good guide to Renaissance editions of classical biological writings is the second lecture in George Sarton's *Appreciation of Ancient and Medieval Science During the Renaissance* (*1450–1600*) (Philadelphia, 1955; paperback ed., 1961). The best English translation of Aristotle's *Historia animalium* is the one by D'Arcy W. Thompson in *The Works of Aristotle*, ed. J. A. Smith, Vol. IV (Oxford, 1910). The Loeb series of classical texts in Latin and English includes Pliny's *Natural History*, ed. H. Rackham (10 vols.; London, 1938–63). Muriel St. Clare Byrne's *The Elizabethan Zoo* (London, 1926) includes extracts from Holland's Elizabethan translation (1601) of Pliny, as well as from Topsell's works. Turning to medieval works, an edition of Bartholomaeus Anglicus is in progress. Until it appears, the reader must be content with the large extracts, in English, found in Robert Steele, *Mediaeval Lore from Bartholomew Anglicus* (London, 1924). A convenient annotated translation of a bestiary is T. H. White, *The Book of Beasts* (London, 1954; paperback ed., 1960). A similar bestiary, *Libellus de natura animalium*, has been reproduced in facsimile by J. I. Davis (London, 1958). For a version of the *Physiologus*, with facsimile text and English translation, see Alan Wood Rendell's *Physiologus. A Metrical Bestiary of Twelve Chapters by Bishop Theobald, Printed at Cologne, 1492* (London, 1928).

Of several nineteenth-century books devoted to the animals and plants referred to by Shakespeare and the literary men of his time, some can still be read with profit. The most authoritative study of Shakespeare's birds is James E. Harting, *The Ornithology of Shakespeare* (London, 1871; reprinted as *The Birds of Shakespeare*, Chicago, 1965). Scientific and unsentimental as this study is, we discover that Shakespeare's acquaintance with birds was quite limited. H. W. Seager's *Natural History in Shakespeare's Time* (London, 1896) arranges the animals alphabeti-

78

cally and provides a convenient anthology of quotations on them from the literature as well as works on natural history of the period. The book includes reproductions of woodcuts from the *Hortus sanitatis* and Topsell. On the other hand, in Emma Phipson's still useful *The Animal Lore of Shakespeare's Time* (London, 1883), the sources are almost purely literary. T. F. Thiselton-Dyer's *Folk Lore of Shakespeare* (New York, 1884) includes good sections on plants and animals. Indeed, Thiselton-Dyer is always worthwhile reading on the subject. Thomas P. Harrison's *They Tell of Birds* (Austin, Texas, 1956) is a modern comparative study of four poets, Chaucer, Spenser, Milton, and Drayton. Harrison shows delightfully and persuasively that Drayton's knowledge of birds was far greater than either Spenser's or Milton's.

The famous herbals by Turner (1568), Lyte (1578), and Gerard (1597) have never been reprinted in modern times; there is only an edition of extracts from Thomas Johnson's edition of Gerard (1636) by Marcus Woodward, optimistically called *Gerard's Herball. The Essence Thereof Distilled* (London, 1927). One would wish for full-size facsimiles similar to those recent ones of the German herbals by Brunfels, Fuchs, and Bock (Munich, 1964). There is, however, a convenient, richly illustrated anthology of botanical woodcuts and engravings from the period: Richard Hatton, *Handbook of Plant and Floral Ornament* (New York, 1960; originally published as *The Craftsman's Plant-Book*, London, 1909). 1,071 illustrations from sixteenth-century herbals are here reproduced, without text. They are organized by modern orders and families. The emphasis is on the art of design.

Noel Hudson, *An Early Version of Hortus Sanitatis* (London, 1954) is a reprint, with introduction, of *The Noble Life* (ca. 1521), England's first illustrated animal book. Banckes' *Herbal* (i.e., *Here Beginneth a New Matter, the Which Is Called an Herbal*, 1525) has been edited in facsimile with transcript by Sanford V. Larkey and Thomas Pyles (New York, 1941). William Turner's two earliest botanical works, *Libellus de re herbaria* (1538) and *The Names of Herbs* (1548) have recently been reprinted in facsimile by the Ray Society (1 vol.; London, 1965), with introductory matter and indexes by James Britten, B. Daydon Jackson, and W. T. Stearn. John Gerard's garden catalogue in its second edition, *Catalogus arborum, fruticum ac plantarum* (1599) has likewise been published as a facsimile (London, 1962).

William Turner's pioneering study of birds (1544) was edited, with English translation on facing pages, by A. H. Evans as *Turner on Birds* (Cambridge, 1903), which also includes in an appendix extracts from John Caius' *De rariorum animalium atque stirpium historia* (1570). The 1576 English translation by Abraham Fleming of Caius' treatise *Of English Dogs* has been reprinted several times (London, 1880; Washington, D.C., 1945; also in Edward Arber's *An English Garner*, Vol. III, 1880). This treatise is included in *The Works of John Caius, M.D.*, edited by E. S. Roberts with a memoir of his life by John Venn (Cambridge, 1912).

Topsell has been well taken care of. We have already referred to the extracts in M. St. Clare Byrne's *The Elizabethan Zoo*. Very recently his two animal books have been reprinted in their entirety, together with Moffet's *Theater of Insects* from the 1658 edition, in photographic facsimile as *The History of Four-Footed Beasts and Serpents and Insects,* with a very brief introduction by Willy Ley (3 vols.; New York, 1967). The University of Texas Press will shortly publish an edition of Topsell's manuscript on birds, "The Fowls of Heaven," by T. P. Harrison and F. D. Hoeniger.

John White, who accompanied Thomas Hariot to Roanoke, made many impressive colored drawings of American Indians as well as of some birds and insects. These have been superbly reproduced in a sumptuous work by Paul H. Hulton and David B. Quinn, *The American Drawings of John White, 1577–1590, with Drawings of European and Oriental Subjects* (2 vols.; London and Chapel Hill, N.C., 1964). White's drawings of North American birds are juxtaposed with Topsell's water colors, which were derived from them but are usually inferior, in a charming little booklet by Thomas P. Harrison, *John White and Edward*

Topsell: The First Water Colors of North American Birds (Austin, Texas, [1964]). Finally, for the history of tobacco and the literature on tobacco, there exists no more splendid and complete work than the famous illustrated catalogue of the Arents Collection, now housed in the New York Public Library: *Tobacco, Its History Illustrated by the Books, Manuscripts and Engravings in the Library of George Arents, Jr.*, with introduction and notes by Jerome E. Brooks (5 vols.; New York, 1937–52). Its first volume is devoted to our period.